REPORT
2007
A MAN'S GUIDE TO WOMEN

REPORT
2007

A MAN'S GUIDE TO WOMEN

THE SECRET TRICKS AND
EXPERT TECHNIQUES
EVERY GUY NEEDS TO GET
THE SEX HE WANTS

RODALE

Book design by Joanna Williams

ISBN 13: 1-59486-535-0

ISBN 10: 1-59486-535-3

2 4 6 8 10 9 7 5 3 1 hardcover

Visit us on the Web at www.menshealth.com, or call us toll-free at (800) 848-4735.

We inspire and enable people to improve their lives and the world around them
For more of our products visit **rodalestore.com** or call 800-848-4735

Sex and Values at Rodale

We believe that an active and healthy sex life, based on mutual consent and respect between partners, is an important component of physical and mental well-being. We also respect that sex is a private matter and that each person has a different opinion of what sexual practices or levels of discourse are appropriate. Rodale is committed to offering responsible, practical advice about sexual matters, supported by accredited professionals and legitimate scientific research. Our goal—for sex and all other topics—is to publish information that empowers people's lives.

CONTENTS

INTRODUCTION

COMPILING AN ANNUAL REPORT on sex and relationship advice is a tough job, but somebody's got to do it. Each year we uncover the best new information about what's going on under the covers and bring it to you in this book: *A Man's Guide to Women*. And each year we continue to be surprised by how much we still didn't know about the opposite sex.

For example, in this book, you'll learn eight ways to make yourself irresistible. That's just one part of our "Get Noticed" section, which talks about how to remake yourself to make women more attracted to you. You'll also learn how to look decades younger and command respect.

In the "Understand Women" section, you'll discover 20 things you don't know about the woman you're dating. We also dispel some very persistent myths about sex and take a blow-by-blow look at how and why women climax.

Next, in the "Date Great" section, we'll let you in on the secrets behind five finer points of dating and help you avoid some common pitfalls. You'll also learn what happens when she's had a threesome and you haven't.

"Sex Secrets" provides everything you need to know to make her happy, from 9 ways to be a much better lover, to 13 ways to spice up your sex life, to what 2,143 women told us about their orgasms.

In our "Get Better" section, we talk about problems we hope you never have to deal with, including how to get out of a rut in the bedroom, how to spot a problem with your penis before it gets serious (not that any problem down there would be comical), and how to deal with conflict in your marriage.

Speaking of marriage, it's front and center in the "Survive Relationships" section. Besides 18 ways to enhance your relationship, here you'll learn how to shack up without slipping up, some great places where you and your other half can get away from it all, and our perfect formula for a pain-free marriage.

Each part of this book also includes some Quickies—which are short takes on the topic at hand—a Guy List of super-concentrated info, Q and A's from the very lovely Girl Next Door, and, of course, a *Man's Guide* quiz.

In short, we offer you *our* best so you can give her *your* best.

—COURTNEY CONROY
EDITOR

GET NOTICED

Before the boy *gets* the girl, he has to *meet* her. And in our drive-through, fast-forward world, it can be hard to attract notice. Most women are too busy frantically trying to check off items on their to-do lists to so much as look up from their BlackBerries. This section will help you catch any girl's eye. Here you'll learn how to shave a decade off your looks with a day's worth of tips. You'll discover seven secrets of success from five wise guys who broke the rules. And you'll find eight ways to make yourself totally irresistible. No BlackBerry can compete with that!

8 Ways to Make Yourself Irresistible

BY NICOLE BELAND

1. Plan that trip you've been putting off. Think big: hiking in Bolivia, wreck diving off Fiji, kayaking Norway's fjords. A man who's about to go on—or is just back from—a ballsy adventure emits an irresistible glow.

2. Get a $100 haircut. Go to an upscale, unisex salon and ask for the owner or head stylist. Don't let a recent beauty-school grad touch those locks.

3. Browse organic markets. Healthy, happy, successful single women channel unused sexual energy into a deep hatred of pesticides.

4. Become a regular at someplace plush. Find a hip, bustling bar or restaurant in your hood and go once a week—with friends, with co-workers, or alone. Tip well. After a month, you'll have a rapport with the staff that, at best, could lead to introductions and invitations. At the least, it will impress a date when you finally take one there.

5. Renovate a room. Find women in the world of interior decorating. From looking for furniture, to picking out paint, to browsing for light fixtures, you'll be surrounded by single ladies. Breaking the ice is as easy as asking her opinion.

6. Throw a bash. Or pay talented people to throw one for you. Hire a caterer, a bartender, and a DJ and invite everyone you know. It's expensive, but the exposure is worth it.

7. Read Gabriel García Márquez novels in public. Women figure if you understand Márquez, you can't possibly be bad in bed.

8. Donate your time or money. Find a glitzy nonprofit—something involving art, music, or theater. It'll add more events to your social calendar, more clout to your character, and more valid opportunities to meet professional dancers.

Look Decades Younger

Shave off the years with a day's worth of tips

BY TREVOR THIEME AND LINDSEY ASPINALL

PICTURE JIMMY CARTER IN 1976. Then picture his haggard visage in 1980. That's what stress, frequent air travel, and politics can do to your mug and body. Maybe you don't have to deal with Beltway-caliber backstabbers, but when you finally have to stare down your own Ayatollah Khomeini, how can you feel, act, and look like the leader you know you are?

"As much as we hate to admit it, appearances matter," says New York City–based image consultant Elena Castaneda. This isn't news to you. You know all too well how your CEO smiles approvingly at the Topher Graces rising through the ranks and how easy it is to peg the over-35 crowd in the halls. How do you polish your image so you can most effectively show off the stuff that matters—your intellect and experience? What can you do to turn back time in the days leading up to a major corporate showdown? Here are 15 ways to put on a more youthful face.

SLEEP WITH AN EXTRA PILLOW

When you sleep, gravity pools fluid around your lower eyelids, where the skin is soft and elastic, causing under-eye puffiness. To avoid the bags, slip an extra pillow under your head. This will encourage gravity to drain the eye area. Chilled spoons also work. The contour of the spoons will fit perfectly over your eyes, and the metal will remain cold just long enough to be effective, about 10 minutes.

PUT ON AN ACT

"People don't remember facts and figures, they remember impressions," says Karen Friedman, an award-winning news anchor and president of Karen Friedman Enterprises, which helps CEOs and celebrities become more effective communicators. To leave an impression of strength, youth, and vitality, be more animated. It'll make you come across as commanding, credible, authoritative, and confident. Practice your delivery in front of a friend or a mirror, keeping these tips in mind:

> Number of years younger a woman will look to you if you've recently been exposed to the scent of pink grapefruit: **6**

PROJECT YOUR VOICE. A booming voice sounds more youthful than a whisper. Imagine you are talking directly to a person in the back of the room.

SPEAK SLOWER. Quick talkers appear anxious. Pace your words at around 130 per minute.

STRAIGHTEN UP. "The way you carry yourself sets the tone for how people will respond," says celebrity voice coach Renee Grant-Williams. A hunched-over posture will make you look old before your time.

RUN AND FEED YOUR BRAIN

"Physical activity can make people more mentally alert," says brain researcher Judy Cameron, PhD, of Oregon Health & Science University. In her studies, she found that monkeys who ran on treadmills grew more blood vessels that supply the brain with oxygen and sugar-rich blood, the fuel that powers the brain. And even a single bout of aerobic exercise floods the body with endorphins that will improve clarity of thought. Get in a run a few hours before you go on.

STRIKE A SLIMMER PROFILE

Research has shown an antifat bias in every realm of society, particularly in the workplace, where fit, youthful people are more apt to receive promotions, earn larger salaries, and snag higher-profile projects. You can't slim down in 24 hours, but you can look thinner by making a few strategic clothing choices.

LOSE THE PLEATS. "Pleated pants add 5 to 10 pounds to your frame because they balloon out and make your hips appear bigger," says Barbara Seymour, a communications coach who has represented Bloomingdale's, Neiman Marcus, and RoC.

GO MONOCHROMATIC. Wearing one color from head to toe elongates your look, according to Seymour. Dark tones enhance the effect.

ADD SOME NONCONFORMIST COLOR. A bold necktie transmits youthfulness. Add a pocket square for flair. Make sure it's in the same color family as the tie, but in a different pattern.

WEAR WHAT FITS. "Tight clothes make you look heavier because you bulge everywhere, and loose ones make you look like you're hiding something," says Seymour. "If everything fits just right, you can give the illusion of thinness."

CHEW GUM, REACT QUICKER

Avoid caffeine when you need to be at your sharpest; its effects don't last. Instead, chew peppermint or cinnamon gum or suck on peppermint hard candy. Researchers at Wheeling Jesuit University in West Virginia found a strong link between the smell of peppermint and improvements in mood, motivation, and athletic performance. That study complements previous research tying the scent of peppermint to enhanced energy levels and cognitive functioning. Another study at Wheeling found that the smell of cinnamon boosts brainpower and improves mental dexterity.

> Percentage of women who say a man in a pink shirt is "hot and confident": **48**

HIDE THINNING HAIR WITH A HAIRCUT

It instantly makes you look younger. And if you are balding or have fine hair, remember that less is more, says Losi of the John Frieda Salon in New York City, whose clients include Harrison Ford, Bill Murray, and Kevin Spacey. Gravity causes longer hair strands to lie closer to the scalp, which exposes more skin on the top of your head. "By getting your hair cut shorter and more layered, you won't see the scalp, which is the whole point. It's an optical illusion," says Losi.

> Percentage of men who would consider plastic surgery: **35**

ADD BEER FOR FULLER HAIR

Any number of volumizing shampoos will give body to your hair. A light lager also works. "The yeast clings to each strand, making hair look fuller," says hair- and skin-care expert Riquette Hofstein.

IRON OUT WRINKLES WITH A TROUT

The best foods to keep skin looking young are fish rich in omega-3 fatty acids, such as trout, salmon, and tuna, as well as broccoli, cauliflower, spinach, and beans. These foods stem the formation of advanced glycation end-products, which cause skin to wrinkle prematurely, according to researchers at New York City's Hoffman Center.

HAVE SEX, WAKE UP YOUNGER

"Sex brings blood to the surface of the skin, dilates your pupils, and gives you a youthful air," says sex therapist Sandor Gardos, PhD. Additionally, going to bed 1 hour earlier than usual will give you the energy of 2 cups of coffee the next day. By contrast, getting less than 6 hours of sleep can decrease your performance to the point where you're operating at the equivalent of a 0.05 blood-alcohol level, says former NASA sleep scientist Mark Rosekind, PhD, president of Alertness Solutions.

Anticipation keeping you up? You don't need to pop Ambien or Nytol. Instead, eat a few fresh cherries or drink some cherry juice. Researchers at the University of Texas found that cherries are one of the best natural sources of melatonin, a popular over-the-counter sleep aid.

NAP LIKE AN ASTRONAUT

In a NASA study, a 25-minute nap increased alertness by 54 percent and performance by 34 percent. Even catnaps of 5 or 10 minutes can help increase memory and learning.

COUNT ON YOUR FINGERS

Rough hands are a dead giveaway of age. And gnawed fingernails suggest that you never grew up. People notice hands the way they notice shoes, says Seymour. Trim your nails with a nail clipper and file down any burrs. We won't tell anybody. Next, rub a little olive oil into your hands. It's a natural moisturizer, and it'll soften your cuticles so you can push them back.

EAT OATS FOR ENERGY

Eat a power breakfast of oatmeal (not a sugar-laden instant variety) topped with chopped nuts, raisins, sesame seeds, and low-fat milk. The long-burning carbs and protein will fuel your body and brain for hours. Wash it down with two 8-ounce glasses of orange juice. A recent University of Alabama study found that 400 milligrams of vitamin C per day (the amount in a pint of OJ) significantly reduces the secretion of stress hormones.

SWALLOW B$_{12}$ FOR BRAINPOWER

Vitamin B$_{12}$ helps lower levels of homocysteine (an amino acid that promotes arterial plaque) and may prevent depression and improve cognition. But as you get older, your body doesn't absorb this vitamin as readily from food as it did when you were younger. If you're

50 or older, take 1,000 milligrams every day, says Edward L. Schneider, MD, dean of the Leonard Davis School of Gerontology at the University of Southern California.

PUT ON YOUR GAME FACE

Do your sideburns and eyebrows resemble Neil Young's? Trim them short, then follow this age-erasing plan:

Get rid of under-eye circles by applying Eye Gel with chamomile essential oil ($28) from The Art of Shaving. Or soak two cotton balls in a 50/50 solution of ice water and cold whole milk. This mixture offers an anti-inflammatory and contracting effect.

As you age, the oil glands that caused acne in your teens shut down, leaving you with gecko skin. After you shave, apply a moisturizer, like Gillette Complete Skincare Facial Moisturizer SPF 15 ($7). Or make your own: Add a teaspoon of honey to ¼ cup of plain yogurt, mix, then apply a thin coating to your face. Rinse off after 15 minutes. The yogurt hydrates your skin and the honey repairs small tears. Whatever you use, apply it to a wet face. Moisturizers are designed to trap water against your skin where it can be absorbed.

> Percentage of women who think green is a color men should wear more often: **23**

For fine lines and crow's-feet, try Zirh Rejuvenate ($43), a cream made to stall collagen breakdown, or Innovative Skincare's Active Serum ($110).

RELAX, WARM UP, WIN BIG

Just before you walk into the boardroom, grab 10 minutes for a quick warmup.

RELAX. Drop a few golf balls into a gym sock and place it on the floor. Take off your shoes and roll the balls around with the bottom of your feet. Each of your feet contains more than 7,000 nerve endings.

Stimulating them can trigger the release of endorphins, which reduces anxiety, says Kevin Kunz, coauthor of *Reflexology: Healing at Your Fingertips*.

DRINK THIS. Lemon water. Avoid caffeine, says Grant-Williams, it will dry your throat. Instead, swig from a glass of cool water with a bit of lemon. It'll help your voice to sound deeper, richer, and more commanding. Just like it did when you were 25.

Command Respect

7 secrets of success from 5 wise guys who broke the rules

INTERVIEWS BY MIKE ZIMMERMAN

ANY HOUR OF THE DAY—right now, even—you can probably flip through your TV channels and settle in to watch one of the 600 episodes of *Law & Order* (or one of its two spin-offs), no TiVo required. And for that you can thank the shows' leading men—Christopher Meloni, Jesse L. Martin, Chris Noth, Dennis Farina, and Ice-T—five guys who are so good at what they do, they've come to embody the very idea of success. Each has taken a different path to this point—some came from the stage, others from the street—but they all got here by sheer grit and determination. We sat down with each of them at the Carnegie Club, an exclusive corner of midtown Manhattan that just begs you to loosen your tie and have a single malt, to soak up some of the wisdom they picked up along the way.

LAW 1: WORK NOW, PLAY NEVER

"One of the things about powerful people is they have the ability to make it look easy. You could be on a guy's yacht and having a great time and he's partying, but then he goes down into the hull and he's on a serious f—king phone call dealing with his whole life. The truth is, everybody I've ever met who's successful is a workaholic. Their first relationship is with their money and their work. A lot of people think, 'Oh, once I do this, I can kick it.' It never happens. Be ready to really, really work. The key is to not think there's an easy way." —ICE-T

"In my senior year of high school, I was the quarterback, and the only thing I wanted was to go undefeated. It hadn't been done in 25 years. It was all I focused on; it was my whole reason for living.

And it happened. That experience, for me, was profound. I realized that if you try hard enough, you can bend the spoon; you can shift reality." —CHRISTOPHER MELONI

"I've heard this since I was a baby, and every time I've applied it, it works out: Work first, play later. That's what drives me. What's the price to be paid, and can I dig down deep enough to pay this price? That, to me, is exciting." —MELONI

LAW 2: IGNORE THE BOSS

"I have a gymnasium philosophy. Everybody's been in a gym. You look to the right, you see somebody in better shape. Look to your left, you see somebody who's dying to be in your shape. So you have to be happy in your life and know you can always go either direction. It's up to you." —ICE-T

"There's an old Romanian saying: If you're going to drown yourself, don't do it in shallow water." —CHRIS NOTH

"Trusting my own instincts has led me to great places. When I was younger, someone telling me I couldn't do something was like saying, 'Try.' You get mad at them and yourself, because they make you think, 'I don't know if I really can do it.' Maybe they're right. Then the anger feeds you, and next thing you know, you've done exactly what they said you wouldn't do, and a little more." —JESSE L. MARTIN

LAW 3: FORGET YOUR MISTAKES

"There's a hustler term for setbacks. They say, 'It ain't about the come up, it's about the comeback.' Anybody can come up, but can they come back? That's where you get your stripes. So you gotta pull up your boots, get your sh— together, shake it off, and come back. Winners have to absorb losses. Setbacks are hard. If I'm bitchin', I stop and take a good look at it, because I'm bitchin' and ridin' in a Bentley! Dude! Get your sh— right!" —ICE-T

"Go back to what's good, what's certain, what's always there. You woke up today. Just start walking. Whatever it is, it'll pass. Time doesn't go backward. That's the one real blessing. It happened; it does you no good to worry. Keep it movin'." —JESSE L. MARTIN

LAW 4: JUST WING IT

"You get pretty secure sometimes. You get to a station in life and you say, 'I'm happy here.' But there are opportunities that come along while you're in that stage of life that you don't take because of your security." —DENNIS FARINA

"Opportunity knocks, what are you gonna do with it? With security comes a lack of adventure. Forgo the security and take care of the opportunity." —FARINA

"I've seen myriad diseases out there, some I've been afflicted with myself. Fear of success, for one. There's a lot of 'I've got this, I'll keep this, I'll hoard this,' as opposed to having a sense of openness." —CHRISTOPHER MELONI

"I know a lot of successful people who are childlike, but they're smart. They understand the touchstones along the way that you have to invest in or see. They're open, like a child, to what you need to do as you climb the ladder. It's almost like street smarts." —MELONI

LAW 5: MAKE SURE YOU FAIL

"I think everybody's held back by the same thing: insecurity. Insecurity causes all the problems in the world. A lot of people tell me, 'I don't know how to deal with rejection.' Well, you'd better learn! Be willing to lose, because if you can take the loss, you can win. When things go wrong, on the street we say, 'Charge it to the game, man.' Because there will be prices to pay to move up in the game. Donald Trump has lost hundreds of millions of dollars. He's made it, but he's lost it. You have to charge some to the game." —ICE-T

"There's always that element that it could not work out no matter how good you are, or it might work out even though you weren't ready for it. Be prepared for surprises." —JESSE L. MARTIN

LAW 6: DON'T TRY TO FIT IN

"Today we define success by publicity and bank accounts. But that's not really success at all. Don't believe the hype. Success is ephemeral. You have to define it for yourself." —CHRIS NOTH

LAW 7: ALWAYS BE IMPATIENT

"Your philosophy changes as you get older. You feel what the word *mortality* really means. The spark could go out any minute. You just want to know how much time you're going to get. So I'm searching for some kind of vitality every day." —CHRIS NOTH

"I'm always thankful that I get up in the morning and it's a new day. I don't watch the news too much or watch reality shows. I try not to clutter my mind. I'm not too competitive. It just complicates my life." —DENNIS FARINA

"I got a f—king headache with these questions. I have no idea what I just said. Did I sound all right?" —DENNIS FARINA

"The best advice I ever got was when somebody said, 'Enjoy.' Intensity is interesting, but fun connects people. You can be childlike without being childish. A child always wants to have fun. Ask yourself, 'Am I having fun? Is this my bliss?'" —CHRISTOPHER MELONI

Be Nice

Lots of women love men who have a sensitive side. The trick is
knowing when to show it

BY EMMA TAYLOR AND LORELEI SHARKEY

MEN ALWAYS ASK US why women won't sleep with nice guys. We will.
It's just that jerks have been able to perfect the first-impression pack-
age that catches our attention. And in our years as sex-advice colum-
nists, it has become clear that you good guys can learn from the
players. Just follow these steps to score like a jerk—without becoming
one yourself.

BE CONFIDENT

Without this, you might as well forget the next eight steps,
'cause you ain't getting laid. We don't care what kind of Jedi mind
trick it takes—a *Raging Bull*-style motivational speech in the bathroom mirror or imagining her with a massive zit on her nose—you
should force your body to act confident. Don't slouch, do nod and
smile when she's talking, and put your beer on the bar between sips,
rather than clutching it like a life preserver. Because if you don't
believe in yourself as a sex machine, she never will.

BUT DON'T BE ARROGANT

If you lay it on too thick and make yourself the focus (or, worse,
the hero) of every story you tell, you know what we'll think? That
you're insecure and desperate and have something to prove. We can
spot a Napoleon complex within 60 seconds. What we like instead is
self-deprecation—a guy who can laugh at himself. Make fun of yourself in the past tense. Everyone loves to bond about what dorks we
were in high school. It proves that you can laugh at yourself while

subtly conveying that you've become way cooler. One boyfriend of Lo's won her over by breaking out his hilariously hideous 1995 driver's-license photo. But be careful not to overdo the self-deprecation, lest you fail the next step.

DON'T WHINE, COMPLAIN, OR BITCH

About anything—it's seriously unsexy. If you can't get a bartender's attention, for example, don't sigh loudly and complain about the service—laugh it off and ask her to give it a shot instead. And your problem at work? Don't care! We're drinking, here!

STOP BEING SO CONSIDERATE

Nice guys hate to offend, so they add "just kidding" after every sarcastic comment. It's the equivalent of smiley emoticons. You don't have to be so gushing and eager to please. Poke fun at her girly drink, her jukebox selections, her brick of a joke. You know, the way you made fun of the girls you really liked when you were in sixth grade.

COMPLIMENT HER

But make it about something besides her appearance. She's heard a thousand guys tell her she has great skin, so it no longer even registers as a compliment—she just assumes you're trying to get in her pants. But if you are genuinely listening to her (you are, right? Hello?) and you manage to observe something about her inner person, it will get you far, because it's rare. You could be totally off base, but it doesn't matter: People are always fascinated by a near stranger's assessment of their character. It's kind of like reading a horoscope. If she makes you laugh, tell her she's funny. If she says something sweet, tell her she's kind. If she tells a great story, ask if you can steal it. Years ago, a guy in a bar told Em she had great style, and she's never forgotten it—it's a million times better than "You look hot in that."

TOUCH HER

After you've developed a rapport, find a lighthearted excuse for a little skin-to-skin contact—like a gentle shoulder punch when she makes you laugh, an elbow touch as you click on some shared delight, or a cozy duet at a karaoke bar. Or drag her onto the dance floor to something like Kings of Leon or upbeat Sinatra, so you can swing around together like a poor man's Fred and Ginger. But don't grope or gaze deeply into her eyes while putting your hand on her knee—she'll think you read some cheesy book (written by a man) on how to hook up.

RECRUIT A WINGWOMAN

Wingmen are for beer ads. Wingwomen are for closing the deal. When a woman sees a guy with cool female friends, she assumes (a) he's a laugh to be around; (b) he genuinely likes women, rather than just their body parts; (c) he's not desperate; and (d) he'll probably still respect her in the morning. Moreover, wingwomen—especially cute ones—create an air of friendly competition. Your college gal pals make great wingwomen, because you've known them long enough for the relationship to be obviously platonic. Or, if one of your guy friends has a cool girlfriend, invite them both out: Most women in relationships are chronic matchmakers. Confide in her that you need her help; she'll be flattered. Then let her work her magic.

BUY HER A DRINK

But let her buy the next round. It blurs the lines between pickup artist and pickupee. Let her do a little of the work so she'll relax into being seduced. If you don't, it'll make her more judgmental (and more likely to give you the Heisman). If you insist that she not pay for anything, she'll see you as an old-fashioned control freak who thinks that women who put out on the first date aren't "girlfriend material."

MAKE HER LAUGH

If she's cracking up, she's too busy having a good time to wonder about your motives (not the case if you insist on supersmooth, seriously seductive pickup lines). Sharing a laugh makes her feel you two are "connecting." In fact, it's a far better indicator that she'll go home with you than sharing a kiss. But please, no knock-knock jokes or movie quotes; you have to be witty and irreverent.

Funny stories are always good. Em's fiancé cracked her up the first time they met by recounting how he got chased down by his neighbor's pet monkey after making monkey faces at it. And a cloak of humor can disguise your intentions just enough: Ask her jokingly if she'd like to come up and see your etchings. After all, the truth is often spoken in jest.

Jump-Start Your Sex Life

Simple strategies to turn your old flame into a towering inferno

BY STEVE CALECHMAN

REPETITION IS GREAT—if you're learning Spanish, grooving your backhand, or making sure the sutures don't rupture. But it's death for your sex life, turning the pursuit of happiness into a holding pattern. Over Newark.

Well, enough of that stuff. It's time to accelerate your pulse with some good, clean, original sex. It doesn't mean risking arrest in a public garden—although it could—but it does mean injecting surprise into the proceedings. Yes, surprise—even if you think you know her body better than the quickest route to the local 7-Eleven.

We have 32 ideas to launch a voyage of sexual discovery unlike anything you've seen…at least since Cindy Lou let down her guard senior year. The difference now: You know what you're doing, and you have a partner who deserves your respect, attention, and devotion. So make the most of it. Now, repeat after us, "I will…"

START THE ACTION ANYWHERE EXCEPT THE BEDROOM. The same old place is too conducive to the same old patterns, says Stella Resnick, PhD, a psychologist in West Hollywood and author of *The Pleasure Zone: Why We Resist Good Feelings and How to Let Go and Be Happy*. Explore some new erogenous areas: The kitchen. The bathroom. Quebec City. Your bodies will be in new places, making it unlikely that you'll follow old routines.

COMPLIMENT HER. And keep doing it…at least five times a day. It'll make her feel noticed, special, and appreciated, and she'll feel closer to you. "The more connected she feels, the more sexually inspired she'll feel," says Laura Berman, PhD, director of the Berman Center in Chicago. Compliment what she feels good about and cares about—her hair, shoes, singing voice, work triumphs—says Gloria Brame, PhD, a sex therapist and the author of *Come Hither: A Commonsense Guide to Kinky Sex*. A confident sex partner is an adventurous sex partner.

GO CANOEING OR HIKING. Add a distinct but manageable touch of danger to the day. It will stimulate dopamine in her brain, which may trigger her sex drive, says Helen Fisher, PhD, an anthropologist at Rutgers University and the author of *Why We Love*. Pick the right trip—a guided whitewater excursion, for instance—and learn all about both the risks and the precautions you'll take. She'll see you as the cause of the excitement, as well as the source of security. Book the right B&B for the afternoon dry-off, and you're set.

WATCH PORN WITH THE SOUND OFF. Sure, you'll miss the snappy plumber-housewife banter. But now you two can provide the dialogue. You'll learn how to talk erotically, so it's educational. But it's also fun, you're both invested in it, and it can help reveal fantasies, says Ava Cadell, PhD, a sex therapist and the author of *Love Around the House*. And you'll probably find some way to kill time during the sex scenes.

OR SEE A CHICK FLICK. Maybe porn isn't her thing. But Pitt, Clooney, or McConaughey might be, and for her, these guys are porn, Dr. Brame says. She'll be fantasizing about a man who's sweet and will treat her well. And when he kisses the flirty female lead, you kiss your lady at the same time. Show her that reality—her life—can be better than that.

FEED HER BLACK LICORICE. Bring it along when you're watching the Clooney flick. Black licorice has been shown to speed up her genital bloodflow by 40 percent, Dr. Cadell says.

CRAFT FANTASIES. Some Saturday afternoon when you're feeling frisky, pour wine and divide ten 3- by 5-inch index cards between yourself and your mate. Each of you writes down five sexual fantasies while the wine loosens your inhibitions. Then head out to a restaurant, where you can get a booth and some privacy in a public setting. Over dinner and more wine, pull out the cards and discuss. You'll feel filthy discussing this stuff in hushed voices in a public place, which is exactly the point. Your goal: Make three piles—"yes," "maybe someday," and "not on your life." Put the possibles in a shoe box and, once a month (she feels sexiest before she ovulates), pull out a winner. Any necessary planning—you can't go with just any football player and cheerleader outfits—heightens the anticipation, Dr. Cadell says.

EXPLORE NEW REGIONS. You've heard about her nipples and vagina? Good. Now spend some time on the back of her neck. It's a brave new world of nerve endings, so gentle caressing and kissing are all that's needed. The base of her spine is sensation central, as well. Or gently stroke and kiss her belly just above the pubic hairline. Sex becomes about discovery, not seeking some destination. "Goal-oriented sex is not that sexy," Dr. Brame says.

TAKE AN OVERNIGHT TRAIN. There are stimulators all around, from the dining car, to the passing landscape, to trying to walk and balance a gin and tonic in the aisle. And there's also your sleeping compartment, your own special sex-womb with a view. It's a new place, and it moves, which adds a new dynamic. And it's somewhat public; there'll be new excitement when you're in flagrante delicto as the train stops and people are outside your window.

SPEND A NIGHT IN TIBET. Try the Yab-Yum position, which is how they talk dirty in Asia. You both sit up and she faces you, sitting on your lap with a pillow under her bottom, for easier penetration. You'll have constant contact with her clitoris, but she'll control the pressure. Move slowly. "The emotional connection makes it intense," says Lou Paget, author of *365 Days of Sensational Sex*.

INVITE HER TO DITCH HER UNDERWEAR DURING DINNER. The naked secret you now share will linger through dessert, says Pepper

Schwartz, PhD, a sociology professor at the University of Washington and the author of *The Great Sex Weekend.*

TALK IN PUBLIC. Lie on a blanket in a park, with people all around, and whisper your fantasies to one another, sparing no detail. You'll create sexual tension, but there's safety because there's no possibility of sex then and there. "It's just plain sexy to start something that can't be finished right then," Dr. Fisher says. When you return home later, spread out the blanket on the floor—a different location—and release the tension.

TAKE HER TO AN ETHNIC RESTAURANT IN A NEW PART OF TOWN. Dopamine is an ideal sex lubricant, and in any new experience, the jets are on. When walking in unfamiliar territory, put your arm around her. There's the thrill of the unknown, but you're guiding her through it—a potent mix. "It might make her want to have sex with you," Dr. Fisher says.

VISIT THE EROTICA SECTION OF THE BOOKSTORE. That in itself will fuel your imaginations. Make some purchases, then read them to each other. You'll discover new interests that, amazingly, never came up when you were buying garden supplies. Feel free to enact a scene. Check out *Heat Wave: Sizzling Sex Stories,* by Alison Tyler; *Five Minute Erotica,* by Carol Queen; and titles in the Black Lace series, by Kerri Sharp.

USE FRAGRANCE FOR FOREPLAY. Spray a touch of the cologne she loves on the sheets. A study by Indiana University researchers found that women who fantasized while smelling a popular men's cologne were more aroused than when smelling women's cologne or a neutral odor. If you don't have a scent, shop for one with her. That's foreplay, too.

LEAVE HOME. Plan a trip without the kids, because Mom and Dad must also be husband and wife. (Try Web sites like www.lastminute.com and www.site59.com that specialize in packaged getaways.) Take lots of pictures; in a few months, go through them with her, slowly, and recall all the great stuff that happened—the sights, the food, the long mornings in bed. The feeling will come hurtling back, Dr. Schwartz says—without airfare this time.

THROW THE TV OUT OF THE BEDROOM. It sucks up time, makes you zone out, and takes focus away from what the room is for, says Diana Wiley, PhD, a therapist at UCLA's female sexual medicine center.

CLIMB TO ONE PEAK AT A TIME. Some couples feel pressure to reach orgasm at the same moment. But that's like coordinating Patriots and Red Sox championships in the same year: nice when it happens, but improbable. So on a night when you're both primed to try something different, resolve to go for one orgasm at a time, without intercourse. As a gentleman, you'll insist that she go first, naturally. It will take some practice—and lots of moaned instructions—to get the manual stimulation or oral timing just right. Which can only be good. Focusing on her solo pleasure will teach you useful lessons to employ the next time you strive for the Lombardi trophy together.

EXPERIENCE THE CUBAN PLUNGE. "¿Qué es eso?" you ask, in junior-high-school Spanish. It's sex with a three-chili rating. Here's how you do it: As you assume the man-on-top position, ask her to bring her knees to her chest and drape her legs over your shoulders. Her vagina will be elongated and extended, and your penetration will be deeper and more pleasurable for her, which qualifies as a win-win situation. "You can feel intense friction against her genital area with each thrust," says Dr. Wiley.

KISS FOR 12 SECONDS. As a relationship ages, pecks on the cheek become the default, and they're about as erotic as a pair of baggy sweatpants. A long, lingering smooch reintroduces you to each other. Give her two a day: one in the morning before one of you leaves, and one as soon as you're both home. Mouths open. Arms around each other. "If you kiss like that for the rest of your lives, passion will never fade," Dr. Cadell says.

ADD A SIDE OF POLYNESIA. During oral sex, don't head straight for her clitoris. Try the Tahitian Method instead. Lie perpendicular to her and move your tongue back and forth over the hood of her clitoris. You'll be able to work both sides, Paget says. (Yes, there are two sides to the clitoris. More on that soon.) To receive immediate feedback, place your middle finger on her perineum, the quarter-size spot just below her vagina. When you're working the right place, the perineum will involuntarily contract. Isn't that helpful?

ASK FOR DIRECTIONS. As you now know, the clitoris has two sides, so ask, "Do you like it on the left or the right?" says Violet Blue, a sex educator and the author of *The Ultimate Guide to Sexual Fantasy*. Either she knows and will appreciate your sensitivity, or she doesn't, and now you've given her a new path to happiness. Plus, the question makes her feel more comfortable with giving you feedback.

CLEAN OUT THE CLOSET. She keeps saying it needs to be done, so start doing it together and then tackle her in there, on top of the out-of-season clothes you're going to wash anyway. The room is stocked with ties, blindfolds, costumes, and a healthy air of 4.16-androstadien-3-one—a chemical in your sweat, hair, and skin. It's a potent arousal mechanism, according to a study performed at the University of California at Berkeley, and your clothes are saturated with it. When she reaches the peak of her androstadien madness, have her put on that blouse she hasn't worn in 5 years and finally give it some purpose by ripping it off. "Most women want to be ravaged by the men they love," Dr. Cadell says.

GO PICASSO ON HER. Buy a half-inch camel-hair paintbrush at the art-supply store, dip it in chocolate sauce, and use it to adorn her stomach or thighs—or paint a long line down her back and buttocks. Remove however you see fit. If she'd prefer to be her own Georgia O'Keeffe, have her paint sequential numbers on her body where she wants to be touched. Find your way in order by using your fingertips and mouth. Accounting was never this much fun.

BUY HER SOMETHING. It doesn't have to big. Just take her out, discover her wishes, indulge, pay. It's the *Pretty Woman* fantasy, but this time, you're Richard Gere. "Women turn on to togetherness and being taken care of," Dr. Schwartz says. Achieve a double jump start by funding an erotic shopping spree. Write out a gift certificate with an expiration date that coincides with your evening at a hotel. If she prefers to shop alone, let her—either way, you'll find out what interests her, Blue says.

USE A CHIN REST. Nothing jump-starts her like oral sex, so we'll venture some more advice: Put one pillow under her hips and another under your chest. Her lower back will be more relaxed, and it'll be easier for her to adjust her knees and legs, allowing for more sensation. Rest your chin on your fist, with your pinkie down, and use a finger to put pressure on the bottom of the opening of her vagina to heighten the sensation, Paget says. All good for her.

WRITE HER A LETTER. One that does not involve a laser printer or an e-mail address. You want this to come straight from the heart. Write what you feel, but the ruling sentiment should be one of gratitude and confidence in your future together. Then, lick a stamp and mail it to her. She'll feel valued and special, and not just because you're supporting the postal service, which keeps the country working. "When a woman feels desired, she'll feel desirous," Dr. Wiley says.

TRY SOMETHING NEW DURING PENETRATION. Rather than the old in-and-out, try rotation: It'll make for a different kind of clitoral stimulation, Paget says. And the absence of thrusting will help you last longer.

SWIM. Bodies feel good in the water. You're semiclothed and you're in public, so it only goes so far, but you can play under the surface, which adds tension, Dr. Brame says. A late-night skinny-dip in the ocean means fewer clothes and a little more danger, pumping up the dopamine levels. Throw a blanket down when you crawl ashore: Sand hurts.

TALK BIG ABOUT THE FUTURE. You know her dreams—children, a beach house, season tickets to the Steelers—so tell her your plans to give her that and more. You're touching a primal desire and emphasizing your long-term commitment. "Women like to be provided for," Dr. Fisher says.

EXPERIMENT WITH BETTER GROOMING. That is, trim each other's pubic hair until it's just right. You're making some smooth skin, which is much more pleasing for the 12-second kisses. But it also makes for fun in the shower. It's slow and methodical, but it also allows for some power-playing. She has the razor; she has control. And you determine, with her help, just how bare she's willing to go.

GO AHEAD AND STARE. Lavish praise on the lilies and you'll be invited back to the garden. So concentrate on a favorite body part and talk about how beautiful she is. "Make her feel sexy by thinking and saying she's sexy," Dr. Fisher says.

Send Clear Signals

IT TURNS OUT you can just sit there on a bar stool and attract women. But it depends on how you sit. A recent study in the journal *Evolution and Human Behavior* found that the men who are the most successful with women exhibit a certain body language before they make their approach. Check out the most effective nonverbal pickup language.

OPEN BODY POSITIONING: Men who have open body language—who don't close off their torsos with crossed arms—are seen as more attractive, potent, active, and persuasive.

SPACE-MAXIMIZATION MOVEMENTS: The most dominant man in a group commands the most space. Men who stretch or extend their arms and legs across chairs convey control of personal and physical space.

INTRASEXUAL TOUCHING: Touching your guy friends (within limits, of course) shows affection. Touchers are perceived as having more status and more social power than those being touched—or those who don't touch at all.

GLANCING BEHAVIOR: Men who frequently glance around are more likely to make eye contact with women, and women respond better to men with whom they've already exchanged glances.

Be a Hero

TODAY'S ROMANCE-NOVEL HEROINE—and the estimated 47.5 million women who follow her exploits—is more sexually empowered than those featured in the bodice rippers of the '70s and '80s. "Nowadays a woman can rip off her own bodice, not to mention the hero's shorts," says Leslie Kelly, author of 15 romance novels. "But she still wants the fantasy." Here's how to become a modern romance hero in four easy steps.

UNDERSTAND THAT IT'S A PERSONALITY THING. Before the hero gets any action, he has to win the heroine with his irresistible personality. "The hero is self-confident. He never whines. He's strong enough in his masculinity to be honest about his feelings. He's full of honor and integrity, and he's never cruel," says Kelly.

MASTER THE SLOW BURN. Heroes are experts at mental seduction. "Every time the heroine sees the hero, he does something to make her want him," says Kelly. "Through his dialogue. The look in his eyes. The way he moves. He makes her wonder if he can really deliver what his attitude says he can deliver." In other words, lots of flirting and physical contact: a hand on her back, an arm around her shoulder—small signs that let the would-be damsel know how badly you want to be near her.

BE A SOFTY. A true romance hero lets his heroine know just how much he wants her, says Kelly. Make it clear that you notice every inch of her body, that you're aware of every part of her—even her, um, mind. And while you're at it, give her something without expecting anything in return: a bubble bath with no distractions, not even you. It'll pay dividends later.

SET HER UP FOR POWERBALL. Planned seductions have their place, but spontaneity is better, and less work. The key is in the details and, of course, the foreplay. "It doesn't have to be wild, crazy, up-against-the-wall sex, but it should really take her breath away because she never anticipated the power of it," says Kelly. Think slow, emotional, and sensual. It will leave her wanting more, which is what you want too, when you suddenly charge away on that rented white horse.

Boost Your Sex Appeal

BOOSTING YOUR SEX APPEAL is easy with this advice taken from 900 women surveyed in an Opinion Research Corporation/*Best Life* poll.

BE THERE. At least 84 percent rated "faithful to me" in their top-10 attributes. "Our tendency toward attachment is biological. We can't help it; we want to keep you around in case of offspring." Tell her your plans for the future—for next Saturday, next month, next year. Include her.

LAUGH. Sense of humor ranked high with 77 percent of women. But it's not about telling jokes. It's the ability to smile after a hellish day. "You have something left to give—to us—and we like that."

LISTEN. More than half—53 percent—listed "patient/good listener" on their top-10 list. Listening says "you're important to me" better than any gift or compliment you could give her. How important? Higher than "good lover." Turn off your phone, your BlackBerry, the Cubs game—and say these magic words: "I'm here. Tell me everything." Then listen.

POLISH YOUR LOOK. Dressing well and staying groomed are more important than a handsome face or great body, women said. Pay attention to details. It says you're a man who recognizes quality. "It shows an appreciation for beauty, and I think that's what women are: We're the beauty in your life."

Be Your Best

YOU DIDN'T GET where you are in life without learning a few things. The most important lesson? Never stop learning. To wit:

BEST WAY TO PAY A COMPLIMENT. Be brief, sincere, and original. "That's a lovely engagement ring" has nothing on "On behalf of all bachelors, we hate to lose you."

BEST WAY TO SURPRISE HER. Put flower petals on top of the bedroom ceiling fan and turn it on when she lies down.

BEST WAY TO TURN HER ON. Get sweaty with her. A University of Texas study found that men and women who work out together have more satisfying sex.

BEST TIME TO MAKE A DECISION. Between 7:30 a.m. and 11 a.m. Thanks to our circadian rhythms, confidence is highest and anxiety and depression are lowest then.

BEST WAY TO MAKE A POINT. Power up your hand gestures by keeping your fingers together. Body-language experts say spread fingers communicate weakness.

BEST WAY TO HIT A HOME RUN. Focus on the logo on the pitcher's cap, then on a point in center field, then back to the cap several times before the pitch. This preps your eyes to track the ball.

Be Confident

TAKE A BOOST FROM this list of 15 things only men can do. Sure, women can claim gender advances in so many areas that it may seem like men are obsolete—on paper, that is. In the real world, where bugs need killing and fence lines need fixing, it's a different story—and one worth telling…to a woman.

1. A man shuts up when nothing more needs to be said.

2. He hears that knock in the engine as if it were a voice speaking only to him.

3. He provides shoulders broad enough to carry a child at a fair, a woman at a concert, and the whole world the rest of the time.

4. He shows a son what it takes to be a good man.

5. He lets the women and children go first.

6. He digs the Panama Canal and, later the same day, assembles a swing set.

7. A woman can defend herself from an attacker, but a man walking next to her keeps her from feeling afraid in the first place.

8. He keeps score at a ball game and remembers what Grudzielanek did in the second inning. In 1998.

9. He makes the world safe from Oprahfication.

10. He receives and truly enjoys a $6 haircut.

11. He eats cold pizza any day, anytime.

12. He finds a way to fit her 17 bags in the car for a trip to the pool.

13. He forgives and forgets.

14. He works the remote without looking at it while toggling back and forth between two football games, a Bond film, and a *CSI* rerun, without missing a key moment in any of them.

15. He puts naked women in movies.

ASK THE GIRL NEXT DOOR

The honest truth about women from our lovely neighbor

Where is the sexiest place for a man to have a tattoo?

The sexiest tattoo, in my mind, is the Red Hot Chili Peppers symbol that lead singer Anthony Kiedis has inked on the inside of his right forearm—a thick, boxy asterisk located by his wrist. A tattoo, especially an abstract one, on that part of the arm comes across as introspective and mysterious. It's as if he wants to remind himself of a commitment or ideal on a daily basis, rather than make an announcement to the rest of the world about his strength or character. To me, that's about as sexy as a tattoo can get.

Do women use numbers to rate guys' attractiveness?

My friends and I are more apt to do the celeb comparison thing. So if I were trying to explain how hot my yoga instructor is, I might say he looks like a dopier Jake Gyllenhaal, with lighter hair. And my friend would say, "Kind of like Tobey Maguire?" And I'd say, "Yes, exactly!" We also rate a guy's appearance in terms of how mentally unstable we get when thinking about him. A guy can be "ridiculously hot," "crazy hot," or the ultimate: "insanely hot."

How can I tell if a woman is flirting because she likes me or because she's had a few drinks?

Why not make like a 10th-grader and send someone else to find out? If you have a friend in common, ask that person to do a little reconnaissance work on your behalf. If you just met her at a bar, spread the word to your pal or hers as you sneak away to the bathroom. She'll see right through it, but it doesn't matter; women find it adorable when guys are shy. And if it turns out she isn't interested, at least you won't have to experience rejection firsthand.

What's the best way to sign off an e-mail to a woman I'm interested in?

Skip stiff, generic kickers like "sincerely" or "best," which are too businesslike. On the other hand, buddy-buddy goodbyes—like "peace out" or "later"—are much too flip for a woman you're hoping to impress. And of course, none of these is as bad as a cheesy, faux-European "ciao." Sign off with a simple but very sexy "yours." Girls always love that one. Especially if it just so happens yours is exactly what she wants to become.

Will You Get Lucky?

CHANCE, DESTINY, FATE, LUCK—there many ways to describe how boy meets girl. But you might have more to do with it than you think; in other words, you make your own luck, at least some of the time. British psychologist Richard Wiseman developed the following test to help people determine their luck potential—that is, how open they are to chance opportunities. Rate each of the statements below from 1 (strongly disagree) to 5 (strongly agree), then add the numbers.

1. I sometimes chat with strangers when standing in a supermarket or bank line.

       1   2   3   4   5

2. I do not have a tendency to worry or feel anxious about life.

       1   2   3   4   5

3. I am open to new experiences, such as trying new types of food or drinks.

       1   2   3   4   5

4. I often listen to my gut feelings and hunches.

       1   2   3   4   5

5. I have tried some techniques to boost my intuition, such as meditation or just going to a quiet place.

       1   2   3   4   5

6. I nearly always expect good things to happen to me in the future.

    1   **2**   **3**   **4**   **5**

7. I tend to try to get what I want from life, even if the chances of success seem slim.

    1   **2**   **3**   **4**   **5**

8. I expect most of the people that I meet to be pleasant, friendly, and helpful.

    1   **2**   **3**   **4**   **5**

9. I tend to look on the bright side of whatever happens to me.

    1   **2**   **3**   **4**   **5**

10. I believe that even negative events will work out well for me in the long run.

    1   **2**   **3**   **4**   **5**

11. I don't tend to dwell on the things that haven't worked out well for me in the past.

    1   **2**   **3**   **4**   **5**

12. I try to learn from the mistakes I've made in the past.

    1   **2**   **3**   **4**   **5**

SCORING

12–32: Watch out for falling pianos.

33–44: You're no stranger to luck, but damn those missed opportunities.

45–60: You, too, could be a winner—in everything you do.

2

UNDERSTAND WOMEN

If you're anything like us, some days the woman sitting across the table feels so much like you it's hard to tell where you end and she begins. Other days it feels like she's so different she must hail from another planet. In this section, we hope to offer some insight into that most mysterious of places—a woman's mind. We'll reveal 20 things we bet you didn't know about the woman you're with. And we'll expose 13 more things we bet you didn't know about women in general. Then we'll separate some sexual fact from sexual fiction. Hopefully this new wisdom will help you to understand your woman, or at least reassure you that she truly is an earthling.

16 Female Traits We Refuse to Take Anymore

1. You say to us, "You're not romantic anymore." Fine, we'll try harder. But only if you agree to initiate once in a while, too. Deal?

2. Then there's "You never listen." This is not an inherently male trait. I mean, how many times does a guy have to explain the infield-fly rule?

3. No, you don't look fat. Did we mention how you never listen?

4. If you ask our opinion, please don't get mad when we give it. The color of the curtains shouldn't be a referendum on our relationship.

5. It's just a spider, for Pete's sake. Step on it.

6. We worked a 60-hour week, took out the garbage, did the dishes, paid the bills, walked the dog, changed the oil, picked up the dry cleaning, read to the kids, and gave you equal time. All we're asking for is 3 hours on the couch on Sunday.

7. No more deflecting responsibility for crummy behavior with cute and kittenish responses. You can't giggle your way out of trouble anymore.

8. You know damn well what we're doing in there. Stop asking.

9. Forget the notion that raising kids is harder than maintaining gainful employment. More important? Yes. But harder? No.

10. If you continue to dump on our best friends, we will probe the (many) character tics of all your friends.

11. If you want to have kids, you have to have sex. This is not a complaint. This is science.

12. Somewhere, somehow, women were sold this idea of "fashionably late." Men don't get this. Make up a fashion emergency if you must, but don't ask us to be intentionally tardy. It's like asking us to kick the host in the groin.

13. Yes, that woman is hot. Yes, we appreciate beauty. That's why we're with you.

14. We do listen. And empathize. But when your troubles have been analyzed until there's nothing left to talk about, can we please stop talking about them?

15. If we fell in love with you when you had long hair, we're going to want you to keep your long hair until death do us part. We'll beg, but would prefer not to.

16. As for commitment ultimatums, just address numbers 1 through 15 on this list, then we'll talk.

Learn Their Secrets

20 things you don't know about women—revealed

BY NICOLE BELAND

HERE ARE A FEW SECRETS You need to know about the woman you're dating.

SHE MAY LIKE ZOMBIES, BUT SHE LOVES TALKING ANIMALS. Women flash their guy-friendly facets early on, so you quickly learned about her passion for nachos, her George Romero movie collection, and her signature snowboarding trick. But every tough girl has her soft side. It won't be long before she suggests renting *Madagascar* and playing Scrabble on a Saturday night.

Give the cornball stuff a chance. As a mood booster, it's as effective as Prozac.

HER ENTOURAGE KNOWS ALL ABOUT YOU. As hard as she might try—which probably isn't hard at all—a girl can't keep a new fling to herself. Early in a relationship, you dominate her life, so her friends are already calling and e-mailing for daily updates. If she were any less discreet, she'd have a blog with your name in the URL.

When you see one of her crew, ask how your stock is doing.

THE WORSE SHE IS AT ACCEPTING COMPLIMENTS, THE MORE SHE CRAVES THEM. A babe who barely blinks when you tell her she's beautiful knows she's hot, and your praise scarcely registers. On the other hand, a woman who blushes, looks away, or tells you you're crazy doesn't consider herself particularly pretty. To her, the words "You look gorgeous" are pure gold.

Say them often and watch her melt a little more every time.

THAT SEX TRICK SHE SAYS SHE'S NEVER DONE BEFORE? SHE HAS. MANY TIMES. Women figure that even the most sensitive man likes to feel sexually dominant at first, so she'll downplay her carnal knowledge. In a couple of months, her real bedroom persona will rear its randy head.

Speed up the process by "accidentally" leaving two ties hanging from your bedposts.

SHE BOUGHT THAT OUTFIT 4 HOURS AGO. It feels wrong to wear an old dress on a date with a new guy. Since she met you, this girl has blown more than $500 on looking good.

Taking careful note of her clothing—running your hands over a stretch of lace, fingering the bow on her bra, unzipping her knee-high boots—will make her feel that every penny was well spent.

HALF OF HER ECSTATIC MOANS ARE TOTAL BS. You could be stimulating every one of her erogenous zones, but the odds that she's having monster orgasms right off the bat are low. The majority of women are far too self-conscious at the beginning of a relationship to totally let go, so we fake it till we make it.

Don't worry; just last as long as you can.

HER JOB IS MORE IMPRESSIVE THAN SHE LETS ON. Don't believe her when she says her title isn't as VIP as it sounds. Women tend to be modest when it comes to work, in part because they don't base their self-worth entirely on their career status.

Talk up her career when introducing her to others to give her the credit she deserves.

HOW SHE FEELS ABOUT YOU IS WRITTEN ALL OVER HER FACE. If she's into you, she'll grin like an idiot when you enter a room. If she stands up and walks toward you, she's downright smitten.

Unless you want her to curb her enthusiasm, respond in kind when she makes an entrance.

SHE'S PICTURING WHAT YOU'LL LOOK LIKE IN 10 YEARS. From your posture to your waistline, she's evaluating how well you're likely to age, especially if you're older than she is. She wants to make sure you aren't going to turn out like her beer-bellied, couch-potato dad.

Allay her fears by mentioning the adventure trips you've booked. Then maintain the body you'll need for them.

IT TAKES HER 20 MINUTES TO WRITE YOU A ONE-LINE E-MAIL. Don't think that, just because it's all in lowercase and there's one misspelled word, she shot off that e-mail without a thought. She revised and read it out loud until it seemed pithy yet spontaneous.

Every time you shoot back an even wittier reply, you kick her lust meter up a notch.

WHATEVER YOU SAY WILL BE HELD AGAINST YOU, EVENTUALLY. Early on, you might feel free to say all sorts of things about drugs you've tried, actresses you'd love to sleep with, or your buddy's bachelor party. She'll appear to take it in stride, but in fact she's storing the details for future fights.

Instead of censoring yourself, stump her with "If we can't be open with each other, what's the point of being in an intimate relationship?"

REFUSE TO TELL A LIE AND SHE'S SURE TO SWOON. Most people have flexible morals. They wouldn't steal anything, but they don't bother to correct a cashier if she hands back an extra $5 in change. Your date secretly hopes that you'll turn out to be as upstanding as Superman.

Casually and consistently do the right thing and she'll consider you a rare find.

SHE'S GATHERING CLUES ABOUT YOUR LAST GIRLFRIEND. If she could, she would track down your ex and interview her about what you're like and why the two of you didn't work out. But she's not a psycho, so she waits for you to disclose tidbits that she can piece together.

It's simple: Don't talk about former flames.

SHE'S JUDGING YOU BY YOUR BOOKS. The movies and albums you own tell a girl a lot about your personality, but it's the titles on your bookshelves that she's interested in. Back issues of *Motor Trend* and dog-eared Tom Clancy paperbacks won't win you any love.

You'll earn points for biographies, history, Eastern philosophy, and literary novels. It helps if you've actually read some of them.

SHE FEARS COMMITMENT, TOO. She just doesn't realize it. Before long, she'll start nudging your relationship to the next level, because that's what women are trained to do from birth. Deep inside, she's just as unsure about what she wants and reluctant to give up her independence. That's why, when she finally is your girlfriend, she'll start freaking out.

Defuse her doubt-induced mood swings with a female tranquilizer, aka a bear hug.

Surprise! She Already Knows . . .

. . . **that question you asked online.** In addition to Googling your name, a Web-savvy babe will also do a search for your e-mail address. She'll find any sites where you might have made your address public, from classified ads to geeky tech forums.

. . . **your astrological profile.** *The Secret Language of Birthdays: Personology Profiles for Each Day of the Year* is a prized reference book among ostensibly intelligent women. She'll check how your birthday has shaped your personality and relationships. Bunch of crap? Maybe, but it's a lot of fun.

. . . **where you buy your clothes.** She can tell where you shop, and that reveals whether you appreciate the finer things in life. A man who buys his button-downs at Pink instead of J.C. Penney is more likely to suggest a vacation in Palau than in Orlando.

. . . **when you're exaggerating.** By the age of 25, most women have been hit on by dozens of Owen Wilson/Vince Vaughn types and are skilled at (1) knowing when men are trying to impress them and (2) smiling and nodding as if they believe every word.

. . . **how ready you are to settle down.** Shhh, you don't have to say a thing. They can gauge your marriage potential by the condition of your plants, the photos of family members on your fridge, how you treat your dog, and whether you like to watch HGTV.

Uncover the Mysteries of Sex

13 things you never knew about the opposite sex

BY NICOLE BELAND

IS THERE ANYTHING LEFT to discover about America's favorite after-dark activity? Yes! Yes! Yes!

According to people who know about these things, the average woman has sex anywhere from a few times per week to a few times per month. We did the math and figured out that, per year, that adds up to . . .

Uh, actually we had a little trouble with the math.

But we do know this: Women have sex a lot, but men still understand relatively little about what's really happening to a woman between the sheets. No, we don't mean where the body parts go. We mean more vexing matters. Like why do some things turn us on and some things turn us off? Why do our bodies work the way they do? And why do we sometimes laugh after sex?

Fortunately, there are people who know about these things, and we talked to a batch of them. Don't consider your sexual education complete until you know . . .

WHY WE SOMETIMES CRY (OR LAUGH) AFTER SEX. Perhaps it's your insistence on humming Celine Dion songs during intercourse, but more likely it's a physiological reaction. "An orgasm instigates the release of powerful hormones, such as dopamine, epinephrine, and oxytocin, all of which rile the emotions," says Pepper Schwartz, PhD, author of *Everything You Know About Love and Sex Is Wrong*. The good news: You should consider giggles (or tears) a reassuring sign about the status of your relationship. If getting physical with you can move your woman that much, it's probably because you have a profound, intimate relationship.

WHY BOOTS MAKE US FEEL LIKE BAD GIRLS. There is an indescribable transformation that takes place when a woman steps into a pair of knee-high boots, whether they have chunky soles or spiked 3-inch heels. Images of Wonder Woman, go-go dancers, and rock stars flash across our subconscious, not to mention soldiers, revolutionaries, royalty, and pirates. In short, we feel and look like a badass. "There's an enormous amount of symbolism in the tall boot that we register immediately," says Gloria Brame, PhD, a sex therapist based in Athens, Georgia. "Because of their historical associations, boots give us a feeling of added protection while at the same time increasing our sense of power, and that translates into a very sexy feeling that's almost predatory." Grrrowl!

WHY WE'RE NOT THE ONLY ONES IN THE RELATIONSHIP WITH NIPPLES. In the very first stages of life, every fetus starts out as a female. "Males only become males with the addition of greater amounts of testosterone, which suppresses the development of female sex organs," says Sandor Gardos, licensed sex therapist and founder of Mypleasure. com. Hard evidence for that fact can be found about a quarter of the way down your chest in the form of two round, pinkish milk ducts. Nearly all mammalian embryos are decked out with mammary tissue from the get-go in preparation for future motherhood. So behind your nipples lie the dusty, unused pipes and machinery that would have been used to breastfeed little Junior.

WHY THE CLITORIS IS LIKE AN ICEBERG. Simple, really: You see only the tip. Attached to that euphoric pink knob (which, by the way, packs 8,000 nerve endings—twice as many as the penis) is a shaft three times its size. During arousal, this shaft fills with blood and pushes the knob out from under its hood. And that's not all. Attached to the base of the shaft are two arms that descend in a wishbone shape down the sides of the labia and back toward the thigh muscles. There are also two "bulbs" of erectile tissue located on either side of the vaginal opening. The going theory is that they help transmit sensation from the vagina to the clitoris. During the last stages of arousal, the domino effect sets in and electrifies just about every nerve ending below her belly button.

WHY FAT, HAIRY MEN DISPLAY THEIR BODIES PROUDLY ON THE BEACH, BUT WE WON'T EVEN HAVE SEX WITH THE LIGHTS ON. There you are enjoying the sand, sun, and sound of the waves when along strolls a Jack Black look-alike in a Speedo. Meanwhile, the women on the beach refuse to sit at a 90-degree angle for fear a half-inch roll of fat will appear in their midsections. "There's a core contingent of guys who were taught to believe that a man's looks aren't anywhere near as important as his money or status," Dr. Brame says. In other words, when Donald Trump looks in the mirror, he sees the male equivalent of Beyoncé staring back. Because these plus-size guys don't associate their self-worth with a six-pack, they don't care if the lights are on, the sheets are off, and the flesh is everywhere.

Science of Sex

Don't show off to get the girl. Women prefer mates who are risk avoiders, not risk takers, according to a new study published in the journal *Evolution and Human Behavior*. In the study, 52 women were given descriptions of fictional men who decided whether or not to engage in physically dangerous activities—climbing a steep mountain, traveling alone in treacherous terrain, or jumping into a river to save a child. The ladies admired the men who took heroic risks—trying to rescue a child—but weren't impressed by pointless daredevilry that could result in death. "A woman wants a mate who's going to survive to continue being a provider and protector for their children and her," says study author William Farthing, PhD, a professor of psychology at the University of Maine.

WHY HEIDI KLUM IS HOT TO MEN AND WOMEN. Plenty of women find feminine curves sexually alluring. It has nothing to do with our sexual orientation. It's actually a preconditioned gut reaction. "As we grow up, both men and women are taught to view women's bodies as sexual symbols," Dr. Schwartz says. When women see an attractive woman in a bikini or an actress in a tight dress and high heels, our

Percentage of moms who are happy with their sex lives: **67**

brain instantly associates those images with sex. For a lot of us girls, though, it prompts a flood of far less sexy thoughts like "I wonder if she does yoga or Pilates?" that often causes that spark to quickly fizzle.

WHY WE SHOULD DIAL "O" ON THE PINK TELEPHONE. Beating the bishop, waxing the dolphin, spanking the monkey—there's no end to the euphemisms for male masturbation. So why not for women? "Society is more permissive with males, both in what they can do sexually and how they can talk about their sexual behaviors," says Yvonne K. Fulbright, author of *The Hot Guide to Safer Sex*. Indeed, most boys start stimulating themselves silly by age 13. Girls are slower to start exploring and hardly ever talk about it openly until they're well into their twenties, if ever. But there's hope, as women start to loosen up and make light of what happens when they're alone and horny. "Every year more and more women are browsing for vibrators as comfortably as they would beauty products," says Claire Cavanah of the sex boutique Toys in Babeland. Some slang terms she's hearing for female masturbation: polish your pearl, pet your bunny, water your flower, paddle the pink canoe, tiptoe through the two lips, and dial "O" on the pink telephone.

WHY WOMEN'S MAGAZINES AREN'T PACKED WITH VIAGRA ADS. When a woman pops a Viagra, it has the same physical effect as when a man takes one. Blood rushes to her genitals, causing vaginal swelling that's identical to arousal. The difference is that when a guy gets a hard-on, he instantly craves sex. Getting a woman in the mood is far more complicated. "Very few women have sexual difficulty because of a lack of bloodflow," says Jed Kaminetsky, MD, clinical assistant professor of urology at New York University. "The two most common problems are lack of desire and difficulty with orgasm, and they involve everything from relationship issues to self-esteem to hormone fluctuations." So forget the miracle pill for now. We'll have to continue to make do with dimming the lights and downing a martini.

WHY SEX LEAVES US SOARING, NOT SNORING. Women complain about guys passing out the second sex is over. But we shouldn't whine—we should gloat. For you, the rush ends abruptly. For us, sex isn't over even when it's over. "It can take [women] anywhere from 15 to 30 minutes to come down from an orgasm," says Fulbright, "with bodily changes including reduced breast swelling, the clitoris returning to its normal position, a shrinking uterus and 'deflating' of the vagina, and a return to [their] resting pulse rate, blood pressure, and breathing." Talk about a full-body workout.

WHY OUR PEAK IS HARDER TO REACH THAN YOURS. The *Seinfeld* episode in which Elaine coins the term "sponge worthy" isn't far off: Every guy might not be orgasm-worthy. "There's a very interesting new idea about female orgasm called the 'upsuck theory,'" says Deborah Blum, author of *Sex on the Brain*. The gist is that when a woman climaxes, the muscles of her vagina pull upward, helping semen to reach her uterus and increasing the odds of pregnancy. Some evolutionary biologists suggest that the female orgasm acts as a quality-control mechanism, preventing women from having children with men they don't feel strongly about. If sex with you hardly ever ends in fireworks, perhaps it's nature's way of saying you're not what she wants in a husband and father of her children. If she goes off like a cannon every other night, you just might be Mr. Right.

WHY YOU CAN FINALLY STOP LOOKING FOR OUR G-SPOT. It's named after Dr. Ernst Gräfenberg who, in 1950, reported that some of his female patients experienced intense pleasure when an area on the front wall of their vagina was stimulated. Since then, large numbers of women have reported having "G-spot orgasms." The only problem is that scientists can't quite figure out what's causing them. "One camp of experts believes that the G-spot is the place where the roots of the clitoris crisscross the urethral sponge," Fulbright says. "Others believe that, similar to the male prostate gland, it's its own entity." And then there are those like Terrence Hines, PhD, who, in an article published in the *American Journal of Obstetrics and Gynecology* in 2001, described it as "a sort of gynecologic UFO: much searched for, much discussed, but unverified by objective means." Either way, what's important to know is that the area around the front wall of the vagina isn't always an erogenous zone.

WHAT OUR BODIES HAVE IN COMMON WITH THE LIVER OF A SHARK. Let's discuss vaginal lubrication for a moment, shall we? Turns out it's composed of a daunting list of ingredients, from water and lactic acid to squalene, which can also be found in a shark's liver. "Each component contributes to maintaining the delicate balance between yeast and bacteria inside the vagina," Gardos says. (He had nothing to add about the shark thing.) As for where it comes from, the answer is

Science of Sex

Just nod knowingly if she says she's turned off by porn. Women are just as stimulated by sexual images as men are, but they're less likely to admit it. Israeli scientists monitored brain activity in 30 men and women watching clips of sexual and nonsexual images. Their arousal was equal; brain waves fluctuated by 60 percent in both sexes while they viewed the sexual images. But only the men admitted it, says lead researcher Yoram Vardi, MD, who hopes the findings can be used to develop an objective test of libido.

through the vaginal walls. "The action is similar to sweating," Gardos says. "The walls of the vagina are constantly emitting moisture to keep the tissue healthy, and during arousal that amount increases." Some women get soaked, others are just slippery enough for action. A lack of lubrication is typically caused by hormone changes, dehydration, or a guy who hasn't grasped the importance of foreplay.

WHY OUR WILDEST FANTASIES INVOLVE GLADIATORS. There she is, innocently strolling along in a field of poppies in a sheer white dress. Suddenly she's surrounded by a small army of Russell Crowe lookalikes who haven't had a woman in years. From there the fantasy goes beyond what any R rating would allow. How is it that something that in reality would be so shocking could seem so enticing in our imagination? "Because fantasies, no matter how wild they get, always remain within our control," Dr. Brame says. "Therefore there's no real threat, so you can safely surrender to the illusion." Contrary to what you would think, the fact that rape fantasies are fairly popular among women makes a lot of sense to sex therapists. "Women are often made to feel guilty or shameful for wanting or enjoying sex," Dr. Brame says. "In a rape fantasy, you aren't responsible for what's happening, and that alleviates the guilt."

Separate Fact from Fiction

Do men crave foreplay? Can breastfeeding women get pregnant?
We separate the sexual truth from the boinking BS

BY SARAH LORGE BUTLER

SEX AND RUMORS go together like milk and cookies—ridiculously well. And that's not necessarily a bad thing. Sex is one of those rare topics that we stay curious about no matter how much knowledge and experience we've already racked up. So when someone at a party lets it drop that sex can cure a headache or that oysters make you horny, eyebrows go up and the word gets around.

The only problem is figuring out which gossip is true (sex can cure a headache by increasing circulation) and what's false (oysters, unless you count the placebo effect). To sort out fact from fiction, we asked sexuality experts to weigh in on some of the most common carnal rumors out there. Prepare to be surprised.

ONLY A THIRD OF WOMEN HIT THE HIGH NOTE DURING INTERCOURSE

FACT Intercourse doesn't always stimulate the magic button for many women. And if a man ejaculates quickly, his partner probably won't have enough time for an intercourse-based orgasm, says Irwin Goldstein, MD, urologist and the editor-in-chief of the *Journal of Sexual Medicine*. But studies on what matters to women in bed show that topping out, through intercourse or any other way, is actually at the bottom of the list. "In terms of pure sensation, really great sex is about the prolonged pleasure," says Joy Davidson, PhD, a New York sex therapist and author of *Fearless Sex*. "And there are other ways to orgasm."

WOMEN HIT THEIR SEXUAL PEAK AT 28, GUYS AT 18

FICTION Yes, sex hormones in the body max out around those years. So what? "It has absolutely no correlation to the enjoyment, the activity, the frequency of sex," says Lee P. Shulman, MD, a professor in the department of obstetrics and gynecology at Northwestern's Feinberg School of Medicine. In a woman's late 30s, changing hormones can result in less lubrication and less relaxation in the vaginal tissues during arousal. But sex therapists say that as women grow older and more experienced, what they eventually lack in hormones, they make up for in confidence. So, they'll say it out loud: "A little to the left. Right...there."

> Percentage of men who claim they have faked an orgasm: **14**

MEN WOULD SKIP FOREPLAY IF WOMEN LET THEM

FICTION This would suggest that you don't like running your hands along the curve of her hip, making out in the stairwell, or oral sex. That the only thing that matters to you is getting to orgasm as quickly as possible. In fact, in a 2005 *Men's Health* survey, only 3 percent of men polled wanted to cut back on foreplay. Even the word "foreplay" has fallen out of favor with sex therapists. "I wouldn't call it 'fore' anything," Dr. Davidson says. "The best part of sex is the play." And you can start the game anytime.

WOMEN CAN'T ENJOY QUICKIES

FICTION Women may prefer a leisurely pace most of the time, but they can still get physically aroused in a hurry. Female sexuality researcher Meredith Chivers, PhD, studies women's arousal patterns by measuring their genital bloodflow as they view various sexual images. Turns out that women respond physically anywhere between 5 and 10 seconds after they start watching an erotic film, she says. A woman may need more time to "warm up" mentally—to detach from thoughts and worries and transition into a sexually receptive state of mind. How do you get her brain to play along? Figure out what flips her mental switch most reliably. Dirty talk, a vibrator, a cowboy hat and lasso—hey, whatever works.

A WOMAN WON'T SATISFY YOU AFTER SHE'S HAD A BABY

FICTION The structure of the vagina does change after it stretches to deliver a melon-sized baby. It takes 6 to 10 weeks for vaginal tissue to heal, and longer for the muscles in that area to regain their tone. Kegel exercises—as unappealing as they are—will restore muscle strength. But don't let a woman put all the pressure on herself. As men reach their 30s, the quality of their erections changes too; they're less firm and don't quite have that same salute. More important, Dr. Shulman says, satisfaction is about intimacy—the closeness, the touching, the being together. And what really disturbs intimacy is not muscle tone or erection quality. It's getting up at 2 a.m. to feed that 8-pound bundle in the bassinet.

BREASTFEEDING IS A GREAT NATURAL FORM OF BIRTH CONTROL

FICTION When she's nursing, the hormones that cause ovulation take a backseat to the ones that trigger milk production. As a result, her chances of getting pregnant are less than 2 percent, according to La Leche League International, a breastfeeding advocacy organization. Sounds as good as the Pill and a whole lot cheaper. But—and this is important—it only works if she meets all of the following criteria: The baby is younger than 6 months old, she's the baby's only source of food, and she's still not menstruating. If any of these conditions change and the thought of getting pregnant stresses her out, don't rely on breastfeeding as your only form of contraception. Progestin-only pills, Depo-Provera, condoms, and IUDs are effective methods of birth control that don't interfere with milk supply.

REGULAR MASTURBATION MAKES FOR BETTER SEX

FACT Do-it-yourselfers are more knowledgeable about what pleases them and how they like to be touched by a partner, says Laura Berman, PhD, director of the Berman Center in Chicago. Plus, regular self-stimulation gets your sexual energy going, which pays off in more highly charged encounters with your lucky cohort. In a 2004 Berman Center study on vibrator use, women who frequently got their buzz on reported higher levels of sexual desire and arousal and had orgasms more easily. Encourage your lady to start her engine.

MEN ARE VISUAL—WOMEN ARE EMOTIONAL

FICTION This one gets the experts (especially male experts) really riled up. "Women think men are robots who constantly think about sex and have no deep emotions," Dr. Goldstein says. The truth is, it's a combination of biological and psychological factors that get both men and women aroused. Sure, men are visually stimulated, but they need a heartfelt connection with a partner too. On the flip side, there aren't too many women jumping into bed with men they find unattractive. "In my 30 years of practice," says clinical psychologist Patricia Aletky, PhD, "women have said over and over they are turned on by looking at a hot bod." So strike a balance. Talk, talk, talk about everything that matters—your favorite restaurants in London, the teachers you hated as kids, how you survived your first jobs.

Take Orgasm 101

Here's a blow-by-blow look at how and why women come

BY NICOLE BELAND

WANT IT, NEED IT, have to have it—but what precisely is happening in a woman's body during that clench-the-sheets moment?

It's the only thing that feels better than diving into a cool lake on a sweltering day, biting into a juicy cheeseburger when you're starving, or even getting your wallet back after losing it on vacation abroad. An orgasm is that good. Which is why it bites that it doesn't happen more often. According to several major surveys, only 25 percent of women always climax during sex with a partner. The rest of them either hit—or miss—depending on the night, or never orgasm during intercourse at all. Compared to the male version (more than 90 percent of men get their cookies 100 percent of the time), the female "O" is a fleeting phenomenon. The question is: Why? What the hell was Mother Nature thinking?

That's what evolutionary biologists have been trying to figure out—with little success. *The Case of the Female Orgasm: Bias in the Science of Evolution* by Elisabeth A. Lloyd, PhD, a biology professor at Indiana University, shoots holes in virtually every theory that has ever attempted to pinpoint an evolutionary purpose to the female climax. "The clitoris has the indispensable function of promoting sexual excitement, which induces the female to have intercourse and become pregnant," Dr. Lloyd says. "But the actual incidence of the reflex of orgasm has never been tied to successful reproduction." Translation: Because women can and do get pregnant without climaxing, scientists can't figure out why they orgasm at all.

The good news is that most scientists do agree on the how. Here's what they know, so far—and how that knowledge can help you help your girl hit her peak more often. Because even if orgasms do turn out to be pointless in terms of sustaining the species, they still feel pretty damn good.

WHILE SHE WAS BLISSING OUT . . .

When in the throes of an orgasm, she wouldn't notice if your dog, your cat, and your cockatiel started rearranging the furniture. Which makes it unlikely that she could track all the subtle changes that are happening in her body. Luckily, famous sex researchers William H. Masters and Virginia E. Johnson have done it for you in their seminal work, *Human Sexuality*. Here's what they found:

That warm, sexy rush she feels during foreplay is the result of blood heading straight to her vagina and clitoris. Around this time, the walls of the vagina start to secrete beads of lubrication that eventually get bigger and flow together.

As she becomes more turned on, blood continues to flood the pelvic area, breathing speeds up, heart rate increases, nipples become erect, and the lower part of the vagina narrows in order to grip the penis while the upper part expands to give it someplace to go. If all goes well (i.e., the phone doesn't ring and you know what you're doing), an incredible amount of nerve and muscle tension builds up in her genitals, pelvis, buttocks, and thighs—until her body involuntarily releases it all at once in a series of intensely pleasurable waves, aka her orgasm.

The big bang is the moment when the uterus, vagina, and anus contract simultaneously at 0.8-second intervals. A small orgasm may consist of 3 to 5 contractions; a biggie, 10 to 15. Many women report feeling different kinds of orgasms—clitoral, vaginal, and many combinations of the two. According to Beverly Whipple, PhD, coauthor of *The G-Spot: And Other Discoveries About Human Sexuality*, the reason may simply be that different parts of the vagina were stimulated more than others and so have more tension to release. Also, muscles in other parts of the body may contract involuntarily—hence the clenched toes and goofy faces. As for the brain, a recent small-scale study at the Netherlands' University of Groningen found that areas involving fear and emotion are actually deactivated during orgasm (not so if she fakes it).

After the peak of pleasure, the body usually slides into a state of satisfied relaxation—but not always. "Like their male counter-parts, women can experience pel-vic heaviness and aching if they do not reach orgasm," says Ian

Percentage of women who say they've faked an orgasm: **51**

Kerner, PhD, a certified sex therapist and author of *She Comes First: The Thinking Man's Guide to Pleasuring a Woman*. In fact, Dr. Kerner says, "many women complain that a single orgasm isn't enough to relieve the buildup of sexual tension," which can leave them with their own "blue balls." Don't worry: Like the male version, it's harmless.

BIG "O" BLOCKERS

So what goes wrong on those nights when the fuse gets lit but the bomb never explodes? "Nine times out of 10 it's because [the woman isn't] getting enough continuous clitoral stimulation," Dr. Kerner says. Often, "a woman will get close to orgasm, her partner picks up on it, and [then he either] orgasms immediately or changes what he was doing."

That's why Dr. Kerner frequently recommends the woman-on-top position. Because she controls the angle and speed of the thrusts (have her try a back-and-forth motion so that her clitoris rubs against your abdomen), it allows for the most constant clitoral stimulation. Another solution is to find a position that mimics how she mastur-bates. If she has solo sex by lying on her belly and rubbing her clitoris with her hands tucked beneath her, then you can enter her from behind in that position. By watching her masturbate, you'll also get a better sense of the stimulation she needs.

"Spectatoring" is another problem that can trip women up. "It's when a woman is too concerned with her appearance and/or performance to actually enjoy herself," Dr. Kerner says. There's no way she's going to have an orgasm if she's fretting about her cellulite or stressing over whether her newest as-seen-on-late-night-cable moves feel good for you. Instead, she has to let the erotic sensations register in her mind. She needs to focus, breathe, and let go. "It may seem counterintuitive," Dr. Kerner says, "but [she needs] to relax to build sexual tension."

For her, the best preparation for a big orgasm is probably a long, steamy shower, reciprocal full-body massages—or 10 minutes of steady oral sex. It's not so much her body that needs the R&R as her mind. "Many women need a transition period between dealing with the stress of everyday life and feeling sexual," Dr. Kerner says. "A few

Science of Sex

Twins—bless them—are helping unlock the mystery of women's orgasms. When researchers at St. Thomas' Hospital in London interviewed nearly 1,700 sets of identical and fraternal twins, one in three women reported never or infrequently achieving orgasm during intercourse. Researchers concluded that there is a genetic component to the ability to have an orgasm, because more similarities in orgasm frequency existed among identical twins than in fraternal twins. Up to 45 percent of the variation can be explained by genetics and may be ascribed to such things as hormone levels and the anatomy of the G-spot. What we can learn from this: "All women are different and probably require different methods and techniques to satisfy them," says Tim Spector, MD. "This may be part of an evolutionary test of skill and patience."

minutes of foreplay usually isn't enough." Doing something ritualistic and soothing together that will clear her head of to-do lists, work issues, family problems, and whatever else might be distracting her from connecting with her body is essential for both of you to feel ecstatic.

A HORMONE WORTH GETTING EXCITED ABOUT

The most fascinating orgasmic side effect of all happens in the brain. During the big moment, the hypothalamus releases extra oxytocin into her system. Called the "cuddle hormone," oxytocin has been correlated with the urge to bond, be affectionate, and protect (new moms are drunk on the stuff). Since an increase in oxytocin has been shown to strengthen the uterine contractions that transport sperm to the egg, those findings are giving evolutionary biologists new hope. According to Dr. Lloyd, it's conceivable that the additional oxytocin gives enough of a boost to contractions that orgasm could play a part in conception after all. "Of all the avenues of orgasm research, I think the oxytocin avenue is the most promising," she says. It's even been hypothesized that having an orgasm and releasing that tide of oxytocin is a woman's subconscious way of approving of her partner as a potential dad.

The latest news is that this cuddle hormone might also be linked to her ability to trust. In a recent study at the University of Zurich, scientists asked 178 male college students to play an investment game with a partner they'd never met. Half of the students used an oxytocin nasal spray (not yet available in the United States) beforehand; half used a placebo. Those with the spray containing oxytocin were more than twice as likely to feel comfortable giving all of their money to their anonymous (but legitimate) partner. If oxytocin can help women feel more at ease about letting go and intensify orgasmic contractions, we might all want a bottle of the stuff stashed in our bedside drawers someday soon.

Fulfill Her Every Sexual Desire

The average woman craves sex daily and wants to be wilder in bed. Here's how you can make it happen tonight

BY MATT BEAN AND LISA JONES

EVERYONE WANTS SEX, but no one's talking dirty. Dig deep into the sexual psyches of thousands of men and women around the country, as we did, and this little irony stands out. Lack of communication—not lack of interest—is the top bedroom complaint for men. For women, it ranks second, just behind too-short foreplay.

That's why we brought both sides to the table for a sex summit (hoping, of course, that it'd end with both sides on the table). With the help of *Cosmopolitan* magazine, we asked 6,000 men and women to tell us everything—what they like, what they hate, what they've done, what they're dying to try. The results were as surprising—men and women want sex equally often—as they were enticing: Most women want to experiment and are just waiting for you to ask.

But our survey results are more than just a collection of dirty secrets. Combined with tips from our experts, they're an instruction manual for giving her what she wants, every time, while at the same time indulging your inner freakiness. See, it's a win-win. Let the dialogue begin.

TURN HER ON INSTANTLY

"Women want sex just as much as—if not more than—men do," says Emily Nagoski, PhD, a sex researcher at Indiana University. "But women often feel shy about making the first move." Too shy, say the 66 percent of men who wish women would initiate more often. How to bring her out of her sexual shell? Coax her. Tempt her. Tease her as if she were a cat chasing a feather on a string, advise our experts. Give her a deep, sigh-inducing kiss—then stop. Or pull her close, press tight against her thigh, then move away. "You're letting her know you're open to her advance but making her bring it to the next level of intimacy," says Amy Levine, a New York City–based sexuality educator. Once she's comfortable making the moves, she'll be more likely to pounce when the urge strikes.

STOKE THE HOME FIRES

Unleash your inner Emeril, and you'll nail the top two mood-boosters for women. "When you cook for somebody, it says, 'You're worth my time,' and that's the biggest turn-on of all," says Martha Hopkins, author of *Intercourses: An Aphrodesiac Cookbook*. Our advice: Whip up an easy appetizer, not a five-course meal. A simple asparagus-and-prosciutto dish—sauté the stalks in olive oil for 3 minutes, wrap with prosciutto, sprinkle on goat cheese and pine nuts—is packed with zinc, a key mineral needed for maintaining erections. Follow with a chocolate dessert, and you'll load up on phenylethylamine, a neurotransmitter that activates the brain's pleasure center, and caffeine, which can jolt sex drive.

DANCE HER PANTS OFF

Home cooking not cutting it? "Take her ironic dancing," suggests Nicole Beland, the *Men's Health* Girl Next Door. Go somewhere ridiculous: senior night at a ballroom-dancing club; line dancing, if you both hate country music; a '70s disco joint; an '80s club playing a sickening mix of Dee-Lite, Salt-N-Pepa, and George Michael. "Dancing really well at any of these places would actually be more embarrassing than if you just did the robot," says Beland. "The two of you will goof around, make fun of everyone else, and end up having an amazing time."

She's a serious dancer? Make merengue your mission. "It's the easiest Latin dance to learn, and it's sensual and energetic," says Yuri Datsyk, owner of the Midtown Fred Astaire Dance Studio, in New York City. J.Lo didn't marry Marc Anthony for his looks, after all.

TAKE HER HOME TONIGHT

"She probably won't be shocked if you suggest she come back to your place after a first date," says Beland. But will she say yes? Make this your litmus test.

GRAZE HER THIGH. As you flirt, stand or sit within 6 inches of her. If she seems unruffled, move closer. Eventually you want your thigh to be pressed against hers, whether you're standing or sitting. If she's into it, move on to step two, says Beland. If she squirms, back off.

PLANT ONE, ALREADY. A make-out session is a prerequisite to a sexual proposition, says Beland. Pay attention to how intensely she's kissing back. You want the "I want to eat you alive, starting with your head" kind of kiss, not the sweet little "I'm not really a dirty girl" kind of kiss.

POP THE QUESTION. Your approach can be either funny ("So, what do you say we go back to my place for milkshakes and Jenga?"); hesitant and humble ("I don't even know how to ask you this, but I would really love to be alone with you"); or straightforward and sweet ("Please, God, tell me that we can go home together"). Dial back the sleaze factor and, "chances are, if she's been shoving her tongue down your throat, any one of them could probably end up working," says Beland.

FOLLOW HER LEAD

Foreplay can be a fact-finding mission, not just a necessary evil. Syncing the way you communicate in bed—verbally and nonverbally—will rev her engines more quickly, says Brian Mustanski, PhD, an assistant professor of psychiatry at the University of Illinois at Chicago. He suggests a technique called "sensate focus": "During foreplay, agree that the genitals are off limits. Touch the other parts of her body, using fingers, a feather, a silk scarf, or anything that turns her on, and ask her to describe how it feels," he says. Watch and listen for nonverbal clues, too—moans, thrusts, gasps. Work her hot spots properly and she'll be begging to move to the main event, in which you'll watch for those same signals. The better you're able to read her, the more likely you'll reach a happy ending.

SCORE BEFORE BREAKFAST

The hard sell seldom works. Here's how to heat her up before your waffle pops.

WAKE UP EARLIER. "A woman won't want sex if she feels hurried," says Dr. Nagoski. "Her clitoris won't respond to even the most skilled touch if she's worried about being late for work. And besides, she needs about 20 minutes to reach orgasm, anyway." Set the alarm early or, better yet, make your move on the weekend to ensure that she's relaxed and responsive.

WHISPER, DON'T POKE. Women need aural stimulation to help kill self-consciousness about eye boogers and bed head, says Dr. Nagoski. So pull her close and say, "You're so beautiful in the morning," or, "I love waking up with you." If you're spooning, thaw her out with some sensual kisses to the back of her neck.

BRING HER SOME OJ. Juice masks morning breath, and "the citrus will jump-start her arousal system," says Alan Hirsch, MD, director of the Smell & Taste Treatment and Research Foundation, in Chicago. Bonus: Vitamin C boosts your adrenaline, giving you extra stamina. She'll appreciate that.

FIND YOUR RHYTHM

Don't sell yourself short. "Every guy I've ever, um, known has confessed that he didn't think his penis size was anything to write home about," says Beland. "But they were all perfectly well hung."

Make the most of what you have by using powerful, deep thrusts at a slow-to-medium pace. "It can be wonderfully intense. Pistonlike porno thrusting feels horrible. It can leave a girl dry, sore, and bored," she says. Add side-to-side movement, or up-and-down pelvic pressure against her clitoris when you're all the way inside, to vary the stimulation.

KISS BETTER BELOW

"Being too rough" is the worst mistake men make during oral sex, the ladies said. "Guys think they need to thrust and flick," says Ian Kerner, PhD, a New York City–based sex therapist and the author of *She Comes First*. "But often what she wants is a firm, still tongue— a point of pressure—so she can set the rhythm and pace." Another trick: Ask her to kiss your earlobe with the same pressure she prefers during oral, then cop her style next time you're south of the border.

MAKE A BIGGER BANG

Thinking about baseball or the weather tends to kill the moment entirely, and the oft-cited stop-start technique can leave her hanging. Instead, try thinking about other ways of pleasuring her, says Dr. Mustanski. When you feel your point of no return approaching—it's technically called "ejaculatory inevitability"—treat it as a cue to start stimulating her in a different way. Massage her clitoris with your fingers. Or, while inside her, press against it with the part of your abdomen just above your penis. Or stop and give her oral for a while. "If you're smooth, she'll have no idea you're just trying to regulate your ejaculation," says Dr. Mustanski. "But all you have to do is let your system settle from its excited point."

UNLEASH HER WILD SIDE

Sexual experimentation is earned, not inherited. Unless you're dating a dominatrix, it requires time, tact, and trust: 66 percent of the women we surveyed said they're most willing to experiment later in a relationship. How can you put yourself on the fast track? "Make her feel like she won't be judged," says Candida Royalle, an erotic-film producer and the author of *How to Tell a Naked Man What to Do*. "There's the whole 'slut' complex you have to get past." Here's a three-step plan for jumpstarting her wildest desires.

PLANT THE SEED. The best erotic icebreaker? The written word. "Women like the story aspect of porn," says Patti Britton, PhD, author of *The Art of Sex Coaching*. "But sometimes pornography can be too shocking." A softer touch: Fuel her imagination by slipping a bookmark into a sexy scene in a classic, classy novel—*The Garden of Eden*, by Ernest Hemingway, say, or something contemporary like *The Time Traveler's Wife*, by Audrey Niffenegger.

FEEL HER OUT. Introduce the idea indirectly. Add a steamy, woman-friendly film to your Netflix queue—*In the Cut*, *The Thomas Crown Affair* (the newer one), or our favorite, *A History of Violence*—and use the sex scene as a conversation catalyst. Or reference something sexy you saw in a magazine, Royalle suggests. "That way, you can ask your partner, 'Did you ever think of doing that?' without pointedly saying, 'This is what I want.'"

START TAME. Come to bed in buttless chaps and a ball gag and, chances are, you'll spend the night alone. Try pubic grooming as a starter kit for kink: More than 67 percent of women we surveyed said they'd be up for a trim, if asked (and 55 percent have gone completely bare at least once). "It helps pave the way for more playful experimentation," says Royalle, who suggests offering to let her trim you first. (Ninety-five percent of men said they'd be up for a trim.)

WATCH AND LEARN

Masturbation isn't just her release valve; it's your sex school—if she'll let you watch. "It's very intimate, but it is important for her to share what she likes," says Melinda Gallagher, cofounder of the women's sexual empowerment group CAKE and coauthor of *A Piece of CAKE: Recipes for Female Sexual Pleasure.* Lower the stage-fright factor by encouraging her to guide your hands. Once she's okay with sharing, Gallagher says, she might be willing to start a toy box—or pry open the one she's been hiding from you. No toys? Log on. "Shopping together lets you talk about your fantasies and your limits," says Dr. Nagoski. All without hitting the smut shop on Route 6.

PLAY A GAME

Role playing means more than squeezing her into that old cheerleader outfit. "A woman's sexual thoughts are kinky and creative," says Gallagher. "Becoming someone else can unlock those desires." Translation: She'll be up for acting out her wildest fantasies. "Some women like the rush of being swept away," says Gallagher. So, what are you waiting for, men? There's a damsel in distress in the next room. Go save her.

Read Her Closet

WHAT CAN A WOMAN'S CLOTHING tell you about her before you approach her? Volumes, says Tracey Cox, author of *Superdate*, "Most of us adopt a clothing style that reflects our attitude about life." That's not all, says Ann Demeris, PhD, author of *First Impressions*: "People dress aspirationally—how they want to be." Use this cheat sheet.

> Percentage of women who say they wear high heels to look good for men: **40**

COLOR. Bright colors convey confidence, says Sherry Maysonave, president of Empowerment Enterprises, a personal consulting group. Several colors at once can show creativity, she says, "but mixing three or more strong colors can indicate emotional instability." Wild prints don't mean wild in the bedroom, she says, "just a need for attention."

FLESH. The more she shows, the more attention she craves, says Cox. "This girl likes to be treated like a female. Butter her up with flattery." Form-fitting clothes that cover a lot of skin indicate a quieter confidence. Approach with intelligence and good humor and forget the one-liners.

JEWELRY. A woman who doesn't wear jewelry may have a no-nonsense personality, says Maysonave, or she could be athletic and outdoorsy. Women who prefer small, fine jewelry like to keep things simple. Women who wear larger baubles crave glamour.

SUITS. She's probably efficient and direct, says Maysonave, because suits bypass the time-consuming task of coordinating separates to put together outfits.

Analyze This

GOOGLE CAN TELL YOU where a woman went to high school, but her penmanship can tell you how her mind works, claims handwriting analyst Sheila Lowe. Accurate or not, it's great conversation fodder. Ask for her name and number. Then look at . . .

CAPITALS. If they're more than three times larger than the lowercase letters, she's a narcissist.

SWIRLS AND LOOPS. Look at the g's and j's. Wide lower loops mean she's into sex (or money or food—same urge).

TRIANGLES. Angular lower loops signify hidden anger and aggression.

SLANT. Straight up and down signals objectivity. To the right means she's effusive; left means secrets.

ROUNDEDNESS. Think little mouths. She has a neediness that you'll never satisfy.

LOWERCASE E'S: Broad and open means she's, well, broad and open, as well as a good listener.

LEGIBILITY. Being able to read her name and number is helpful, but careful printing reflects rigidity and the need to control.

Pass Her Tests

WOMEN HAVE CUNNING LITTLE TRICKS they use to measure your romantic potential. Here's your cheat sheet. Your game's a sham, and she knows it: Springing for a drink is nice but ultimately transparent. "Men are always giving off signals as to how they'll act when they're not trying to impress you," says April Masini, author of *Date Out of Your League*. Lucky for you, we snagged the pop-quiz answer key:

THE HOOKUP TEST. Athletes and rock stars get girls because they're cocky and coordinated. "If he's graceful, confident, and calm, then you can assume he'd be better in bed than a clumsy clod," says Nicole Beland, the *Men's Health* Girl Next Door. Air hockey could be her way of giving you a tryout. Our advice: Don't flub the puck.

THE HUMOR TEST. She's ripping on your Journey T-shirt for a reason. "If he can laugh it off or zing me back, it means major points," says Kjersti, 23. "A woman wants to feel like 'He gets me,'"

> Percentage of women who say it takes at least an hour to decide whether a man is worth going out with a second time: **62**

says Dennie Hughes, author of *Dateworthy*. "She wants someone who's just as sarcastic and cerebrally funny."

THE JEALOUSY TEST. Play it cool, but not too cool, when she leaves your side. "If he's too supportive of my venturing out and trying something new—like talking to other men at the bar—I'll take the hint and move on," says Cristina, 24. "If he's silent, then I'll take it that he's jealous, which is kind of hot."

THE BACKBONE TEST. Doesn't matter if she's taking a stand on politics, hunting, or how much to tip: She wants to see how you handle a healthy disagreement. "Women want to know that you have a spine and are able to discuss difficult topics," says Hughes. "Men who can debate with grace are men who will be able to help navigate the difficult issues that occur in every relationship."

THE SERVICE TEST. Shaft the waiter or the bartender and you're revealing your real self. "She's looking at how you treat other people," says David Wygant, author of *Always Talk to Strangers*. Also, be gracious but brief when said waitress or bartender is wearing a halter top with a plunging neckline.

> Women who think synchronicity makes good sex great: **nearly 1 in 2**

THE LONG-TERM TEST. Extra credit: Pass every one of these tests and you could find yourself watching her attack cat for the weekend or spending a day shopping alone with her mom. She's seeing how much you'll sacrifice for her if she's not around, says Wygant. "She wants to make sure you want all of her, including the painful parts."

Sure Signs She's Interested

WITHIN 3 MINUTES of meeting you, a woman knows if you'll ever see her naked. Sadly, she's not likely to inform you of her decision. But you can ask without asking by running these five low-risk tests.

THE TIME PROBE. Forget your silly pickup line. Ask her for the time instead. If she answers with anything other than the time, she's interested. The only exception is "I don't know," but only if she's not wearing a watch.

THE EYE-CONTACT PROBE. While you're talking with her, sustain eye contact for a fraction of a second longer than feels natural. If she holds your eye, she's interested. If she looks away, she's not.

THE WINK PROBE. If she makes a joke or someone else does something dumb, give her a wink and share the moment. If she relaxes or laughs, she's interested.

THE BODY-CHECK PROBE. Make eye contact, then quickly (in less than a second) pass your eyes down and up her body, then look back into her eyes. If she smiles when your eyes meet again, she's interested.

THE COMPLIMENT PROBE. Pay her the kind of compliment a potential lover would make—it should be something personal but not overtly sexual. Also avoid the type of thing a friend might say; for instance, opt for, "You have really great style" rather than "You have a really nice briefcase." If she smiles or thanks you warmly, she's interested. If she pepper-sprays you, she's not.

Be a Top Gun

FORGET A PUPPY, baby, or guitar. A woman is the best date magnet. "Women are more likely to trust other women," says Rutgers University anthropologist Helen Fisher, PhD author of *Why We Love*. Bring along an outgoing female friend who can tell the woman who's caught your eye, "He'd kill me for doing this, but my friend thinks you're beautiful. Any chance you'd join us for a drink?" Or, you can hire one for $50 an hour through Wingwomen.com. Entrepreneur Shane Forbes says he started the site after noticing "I met more attractive, available women with my female friends by my side."

Use All of Your Senses

Hit these 5 targets and win a prize—her

YOU KNOW THAT putting Tab A into Slot B won't make you a pro in the sack. Luckily, you have more than one tool at hand. "Bring all her senses into the experience," says Patti Britton, PhD, author of *The Complete Idiot's Guide to Sensual Massage.* "You'll enhance her pleasure, giving her what could be the best sex of her life." Don't you want to be responsible for that?

TASTE. Feeding Kim Basinger was one of the few smart career moves Mickey Rourke made, so imitate it. Serve up exotic fruits like kiwis, pomegranates, or star-fruits in bed. "Rare tastes are psychologically arousing for her because they seem almost forbidden," says Olivia St. Claire, author of *302 Advanced Techniques for Driving a Man Wild in Bed.* And henceforth, the produce aisle will turn her on.

HEARING. Chris Berman's blathering is not an aphrodisiac. Pick up a nature CD or a sound machine. "Soothing noises enable her to get out of her own head and fully enjoy the moment," says Dr. Britton. If she's worried the kids will hear, put the noise machine in their room.

SMELL. The nose is connected to the limbic system of the brain, which controls libido. So certain scents—rose, jasmine, and ylang-ylang—can trigger sexual arousal. Put a couple of drops of scented oil (available at health-food stores) on the lightbulb in your bedside lamp, switch it on, and watch her get turned on.

SIGHT. "Women respond to strength because it makes them feel more feminine," says St. Claire. "Any activity that involves muscle flexing and heavy lifting will demonstrate that you can take care of her, which is a major turn-on." Strap on a tool belt and do some home improvement. Or, before bed, do some pushups or pullups so your arms look more cut, enhancing your large-and-in-charge vibe.

TOUCH. Rub her from head to toe with massage oil; it's erotic because the slippery sensation mimics sex, explains St. Claire. Feeling more frisky but less messy? With a washable pen, write on each of her body parts exactly what you plan to do to it. Then follow through.

ASK THE GIRL NEXT DOOR

The honest truth about women from our lovely neighbor

Why do women overanalyze and obsess over everything?

Not every*thing*. Every*one*. Relationships—with our significant others, friends, family, co-workers—are what make our world go 'round. So we constantly evaluate them, trying to anticipate, prevent, or solve problems. I admit, we can go too far and drive ourselves and the people around us crazy. But (sorry for sounding like a Hallmark card) it's only because we care so much. Smart women eventually realize there's no point in stressing over what they can't control.

I prefer texting. Why are women so insistent on a man calling?

As a primary form of communication, texting is a little lazy. I know what you're thinking: It's fast and efficient, the opposite of lazy. But women want a sense of how you're feeling at any given moment instead of trying to squeeze a drop of emotion from a few letters and numbers. We want intimacy. And texting makes it seem as if intimacy is something you might be trying to avoid.

My female friend wants me to be her date for a wedding. Does she want to hook up?

Mainly, she just wants a cool, funny guy to keep her company. But if the two of you have ever been on the verge, the combined effect of champagne and close dancing can take matters the rest of the way.

I have a female friend who always calls me by my full name. Is she flirting with me?

Yes.

How to Know If She's Really Single

OLD FLAMES HAVE A WAY of flaring up. "It's not how long she dated an ex or how many partners she's had since," says William Fitzgerald, PhD, founder of Sexdoc.com. "The important thing is whether she has resolved or emotionally withdrawn from the prior relationship." This test will tell you whether she's ready for something new—you—or still has her ex on the brain.

> **1. How serious did they get?**
> **a.** They were like Brad and Jen: hitched, then ditched.
> **b.** They were like Ben and J.Lo: They shacked up but flamed out.
> **c.** They were like Al Roker and food: It was great while it lasted.
> **d.** They were like Paris Hilton and [insert actor/rock star/athlete here]: just huddling for warmth.

The more their lives overlap, the harder it is for her to move on, says Judith Sherven, PhD, coauthor of *Be Loved for Who You Really Are*. Living together means sharing morning rituals, bill paying, grocery shopping, and more. "In that case, a breakup uproots a complete lifestyle," says Dr. Sherven. Give her time to adjust. If you're thinking of getting serious, "wait at least 6 months to ensure that she's not using you as a fill-in."

2. How often does she see him now?

a. They're still "close friends." Sometimes you're the third wheel.

b. They're co-workers or have several mutual friends.

c. They chat occasionally, but it's mostly just polite.

d. She avoids him like the plague.

Here's a no-brainer: "If she spends a lot of time alone with him, it means the emotional connection is mutual," Dr. Fitzgerald says. Be wary if she drags you to his favorite club and then acts surprised when he shows up. "She might be using you to manipulate her ex." If he's a co-worker, it's going to be tough. "It's important that she have the opportunity to miss him and not act on it," says Marilyn Fithian, PhD, a researcher at the Center for Marital and Sexual Studies in Long Beach, California. If she avoids contact with him, she could be suppressing still-raw memories—which means you should ask yourself . . .

3. How does she talk about him?

a. She doesn't talk; she gushes.

b. It's all trash talk, all the time.

c. She's a realist: There were good times; there were bad times.

d. She talks more about herself and how she's changed.

Love or hate—intense emotions suggest an unresolved conflict. "There's still an emotional tie," Dr. Fitzgerald says. "She won't be able to move on," adds Dr. Sherven, "until she realizes that she's a different person now and that whatever happened—good or bad—is in the past."

4. Does she keep souvenirs?

a. Nope, she torched everything.

b. His pictures are still up on the wall, but not front and center.

c. She has his love letters, but they're in a box in the basement.

d. She reads his blog daily and has a shrine to him in her closet.

"It's unhealthy for people to deny their own past, and it's dangerous for you to insist that your girlfriend act like she's never been with anyone but you," Dr. Sherven says. As long as she's not pawing through them on a daily basis, mementos are harmless.

He Said/She Said

Who are your sexual fantasies most often about?

He Said		She Said
30%	Your partner	49%
15%	A random stranger	12%
15%	An ex	11%
8%	A co-worker	4%
20%	A friend	15%
6%	A celebrity	5%
5%	A porn star	1%

We shouldn't be surprised that our wives and girlfriends mainly fantasize about us. "The emphasis on monogamy is very powerful with women," says Gloria Brame, PhD, a sexologist in Athens, Georgia. The bonus: "Women tend to fantasize about their partners performing acts they don't do routinely." Time to change the play, men!

SCORING

1. a = 4, b = 3, c = 2, d = 1

2. a = 4, b = 3, c = 1, d = 2

3. a = 4, b = 3, c = 2, d = 1

4. a = 2, b = 3, c = 1, d = 4

IF YOU SCORED . . .

4–8: She's all yours. Quit worrying about his occasional phone calls.

9–12: She's in recovery. Stop dwelling on her past and give her reasons to forget it.

13–16: She's still hooked. Time for a status check: Is he really out of the picture?

DATE GREAT

The word "date" sounds so innocuous, nothing like the potential minefield it really is. You want so much for things to go right, yet they can so easily go horribly wrong. A new relationship can be very fragile, easily broken. You're trying so hard to impress her, yet you don't want it to seem like you're trying so hard to impress her. In this section, we offer our best advice on how to make your move and make her yours. We also offer advice on how to rev her engine and time your moves so you don't crash and burn.

24 Sexiest Things Women Ever Said

1. "Take off your clothes and turn on the music."

2. Before she left for an extended trip abroad: "Don't worry. You know you own it."

3. "Sit back, close your eyes, and let me do everything."

4. "Let's go get some barbecue and get busy."

5. "Do you want to bring your beer with you in case you lose any fluids?"

6. "If I don't kiss you before the night is over, I'll consider my year a failure."

7. Written on a card that came with flowers she sent him: "This is for the great sex we're going to have tonight."

8. "I would feel so safe lying beneath you."

9. "If you ever discuss your girlfriend problems with another woman, you will end up sleeping with her. So...tell me about your girlfriend problems."

10. "Is your mustache functional, or is it purely for decoration?"

11. "You're my daddy."

12. She pointed to her eye, then made a circle with her finger and thumb, stuck her other forefinger through it, and pointed at him.

13. "I'm going to get naked now. Any questions?"

14. "Show me everything you know."

15. "I'm feeling dirty. I think I'll take a shower."

16. "The sound of your voice makes my nipples hard."

17. "I'll make your bed spin."

18. Bursting into tears just after sex: "I just love you so much!"

19. "Spank me now!"

20. "How the hell did you do that?"

21. "You can have me now or have me later, but you are going to have me."

22. On the freeway: "Have you ever gotten head at 100 miles an hour?"

23. "Give it to me, baby, and give them a good show."

24. "It hurts, but I love it when you do it."

Have a Foolproof Game Plan

5 finer points of dating

EDITED BY MATT BEAN

SHE'S HOT; you're hot and bothered. Which might explain why you're trying so hard to impress her. Just make sure your smooth moves don't have a rough landing. We polled a handful of women for advice on hitting her hot spots—without falling flat on your face.

DITCH THE BOUQUET. "After our first date, this guy sent a huge arrangement to my office," says Susan, 25. "It looked like something you'd see at a funeral. From then on, my friends called him Funeral Flowers Fred." The move reeks of desperation, not sweetness. Instead, take note of her favorite flower and present her with a single stem on your next date, advises Neil Warren, PhD, founder of eHarmony.com. She'll appreciate that you listened.

DON'T JUMP THE "GIRLFRIEND" GUN. "Paul took me out to meet all his friends without any warning and introduced me as his girlfriend for the first time," says Jeanie, 25. "I felt ambushed." Women aren't always as relationship focused as we make them out to be, says Ron Louis, coauthor of *How to Succeed with Women*. "No one likes to feel like you're removing their freedom," says Dr. Warren. "Don't stretch the relationship by jumping ahead too early."

SPEND TIME, NOT MONEY, ON HER BIRTHDAY GIFT. "One guy gave me an expensive snow globe that played the love theme from *Ghost* as a birthday present," says Alissa, 30. "I don't even like the movie. He tried to make up for the impersonal gesture by spending a lot of money." It's true: The thought counts, not the price. "A gift is a way to show your interest, not your bottom line," says Peter Post, author of *Essential Manners for Couples.* Buy her something related to an activity she likes: maybe a yoga book, a framed Tour de France poster, or concert tickets.

KEEP QUIET ABOUT YOUR BEDROOM SKILLS. "On our second date, John volunteered that he loved giving oral sex," says Nina, 31. "Instead of making me think he'd be a generous lover, it sounded like he thought he was a stud and wanted to prove it to me." Dr. Warren explains: "When you discuss sexual intimacy too early, women feel pressured and turned off." Actions—especially intimate ones—speak louder than words.

KISS WITH CONFIDENCE. Asking for a kiss looks desperate. Evelyn, 28, explains this one best: "Just do it."

Resist Temptation

Here's how to handle your smart, young, ambitious, loyal...and beautiful protégée—without ending up in HR hell

BY NICOLE BELAND

CHLOE WAS 22, an art-history major wanting to explore a career in finance. More important, she was the daughter of one of Tom's most important clients. The 38-year-old money manager had an open head count, so he offered her an internship, sight unseen.

Then he saw her sights.

"She was a dead ringer for Audrey Tautou—big, dark eyes and jet-black hair, perfect mouth," says Tom. "She was smart, she was funny, but she was also flirty. I was flattered."

Chloe handled her work like a pro but didn't know squat about office politics. "At the end of the day, she'd walk into my office with a sigh, throw herself down on the couch, and ask about the photos on my wall, which I'd taken in 17 countries," says Tom. "She knew a lot about art and photography, and I was hungry for that kind of discussion. It was easy to get carried away."

The other staffers saw Chloe lounging in his office when they left at night. After a few weeks, they started referring to her as Monica and shaking their heads at Tom's behavior. But nothing officially naughty happened until Chloe began inviting him to gallery openings, where the wine flowed and they started talking about their personal lives. Chloe was having boyfriend trouble; Tom was divorced. After the third opening, Chloe suggested they swing by her place so Tom could see her paintings.

As they say in *TV Guide*, high jinks ensued.

As soon as his clothes were back on, Tom panicked, apologized, and told her they couldn't work together anymore. "She sent an e-mail to my office manager that morning saying that she wouldn't be coming in because I'd f—ed and fired her," he says. "She cc'd her father." Clients started withdrawing funds. Within weeks, two of his employees quit. And Tom ended up moving to another city.

That kind of disaster makes male executives wary about working with a young bombshell in any capacity, even if they're confident of her qualifications and their own ability to keep the relationship professional. And the recent California Supreme Court ruling in *Miller*

The Sexualized Workplace Part I

Men say . . .

Have you ever worried about being judged by co-workers for mentoring an attractive female employee? **Yes 41% No 59%**

Have you ever fought with your wife or partner over an attractive female employee? **Yes 40% No 60%**

Have you ever not hired a woman because you found her attractive? **Yes 12% No 88%**

Have you ever been made to feel uncomfortable because of a female subordinate's flirting or innuendos? **Yes 25% No 75%**

Have you ever lusted after a female co-worker? **Yes 92% No 8%**

Have you ever lusted after a female boss? **Yes 36% No 64%**

Have you ever felt that a female co-worker understands you better than your wife or partner does or that she's more fun to be with? **Yes 49% No 51%**

Do you share things with a female co-worker that you don't tell your wife? **Yes 33% No 67%**

Source: 1,121 visitors to BestLifeOnline.com, August 2005

v. Department of Corrections only raises the danger level: Sleep with an employee, and you can now be sued by her and by all the other employees you didn't sleep with. (The court ruled that workers could sue if they felt a supervisor favored an employee he was having an affair with.)

In this extremely litigious climate, you can't blame a guy for having his guard up. Mixing business with pleasure these days carries major ramifications, as we've seen in the highly publicized exploits of such executives as GE's Jack Welch and Boeing's Harry Stonecipher. "Corporate codes of ethics like Boeing's state that a person can be fired for engaging in any conduct or activity that causes embarrassment to the company," says Helio Fred Garcia, a corporate consultant who teaches crisis management at New York University. "Up against parameters that broad, being cautious is crucial."

Indeed, most executives who get caught with their pants down are done in not by lawsuits but by corporate policies enacted to protect their company's interests. Of the more than 13,000 sexual-harassment cases filed last year, fewer than 8 percent made it to trial. "Sexual harassment has to be severe and pervasive enough to create a hostile work environment [in order to be legally actionable]," says Barbara Lawless, the California employment attorney who filed the *Miller v. Department of Corrections* suit. She cites the recent case in which a secretary was fired from her job of 25 years and replaced by her boss's mistress. The secretary sued and lost because, Lawless says, it was ruled an "isolated incident."

Even so, countless men lose their jobs or reputations—or both— by letting sexual tension in the office go from simmer to boil. Many male managers would prefer to avoid that temptation—and any speculation that they might be dipping into the secretarial pool—by placing an invisible ONLY DOGS ALLOWED sign on their doors. "If I were to hire a 24-year-old who looked like a model, it wouldn't matter if she had a magna cum laude from Princeton and a head full of good

The Sexualized Workplace Part II

Women say . . .

Is it inappropriate to go for drinks alone with a married male co-worker? **Yes 53% No 47%**

Is it inappropriate to go to dinner alone with a married male co-worker? **Yes 58% No 42%**

Have you ever felt creeped out by an older male colleague's attempts at flirting? **Yes 81% No 19%**

Have you ever fantasized about an older male colleague? **Yes 57% No 43%**

Do you feel like you would get more attention from your male colleagues if you were to dress provocatively at work? **Yes 63% No 37%**

Do you feel that such attention would help your career or hinder it? **Help 39% Hinder 61%**

Have you ever flirted with an older male colleague? **Yes 57% No 43%**

Did it influence your career advancement? **It helped 16% It hindered 3% No 81%**

Have you ever slept with an older male colleague? **Yes 20% No 80%**

Did it influence your career advancement? **It helped 14% It hindered 11% No 75%**

Source: 1,451 visitors to Glamour.com, August 2005

ideas—the talk at the water cooler would go wild," says Lawrence, a 49-year-old marketing executive. "The next thing I know, some jerk in HR would be sifting through my e-mails, thirsty for blood."

"The paranoia about bad publicity breeds discrimination against attractive women or anyone else who might call someone's impartiality into question," says Christine Littleton, a law professor at UCLA. The Hottie Liberation Army may not command the same level of sympathy as other downtrodden peoples, but when men discriminate against attractive women, it's a shame for a couple of reasons. One, it's sexism (or sexyism, to be exact), and two, working with a capable, confident young woman can be productive and rewarding in ways different from the experience of working with a young guy.

According to Los Angeles–based psychologist Yvonne Thomas, PhD, the relationship between the male mentor and female mentee can resemble the father-daughter model. "Fathers and daughters tend to have a more playful, cooperative rapport than mothers and daughters or fathers and sons," says Dr. Thomas. "They're more accepting of each other because neither typically sees the other as a direct reflection of themselves." When your assistant or intern is a young woman, it often translates into a more lighthearted and forgiving atmosphere around the office. You'll notice less resentment and frustration and more easygoing collaboration.

Of course, you're not her father. Which means that sexual energy is usually there in some form, either buzzing quietly like a fan in a corner or blowing through the room like a hot wind. But there's no need to act as if that titillating breeze is harboring the plague. "As long as workplace boundaries aren't being crossed, sexual energy on the job can make both men and women feel great. It adds spice to the workplace," says B.J. Gallagher, a management consultant and the author of Who Are "They" Anyway? A Tale of Achieving Success at Work Through Personal Accountability. That energy can be channeled into passion for your work, your workouts, and your wife.

Even so, a minefield is still buried under that Garden of Eden. If you're going to manage and mentor a bright young thing, you need to observe a few rules that will keep the relationship warm and friendly, but never so warm that your reputation gets burned.

APPRECIATE HER INNOCENCE

Even if a woman seems surprisingly worldly and self-possessed for her tender age, like Chloe, she probably hasn't learned how to separate professional relationships from personal ones. "Young women are idealistic and enthusiastic, but they're not business savvy," says Michelle Callahan, PhD, a psychologist and executive coach in New York City. "They still think being sexy will serve them well." It's highly likely that she'll develop conflicting views of you—as a career advisor, father figure, and sexual challenge all rolled into one.

"There's sexual tension between me and my boss, but he is married, and I can tell he loves his wife. Nothing will actually happen," says Annie, a 25-year-old legal intern who admits that she flirts shamelessly with the "elegant and handsome" 45-year-old general counsel she works for. "I want to know that he wants me, but if he were to try and kiss me, it would break the spell; he wouldn't be the man I thought he was."

Sexual restraint is something women secretly seem to want and expect from male authority figures, even if they send the opposite message via provocative comments or body language. "The brilliant man who took me under his wing was everything I wasn't: rich, successful, semifamous, and completely in command of his emotions," says Deanna, 31, who first met her mentor 9 years ago when they hit it off at a corporate event. "I confessed what a massive crush I had on him countless times, and he would just laugh and say something like, 'Oh, good, the love potion I put in your coffee is working. Don't worry, it'll wear off in a couple of days, and you'll see that

When Meetings Have Happy Endings

The flesh can be weak, and lips have a way of landing on each other. When it happens, "take full responsibility even if she initiated it, insist it will never happen again, and express your hope that it won't affect your great working relationship," says Michelle Callahan, PhD, a psychologist in New York City.

Whether the indiscretion was PG- or X-rated, brace yourself for a worst-case scenario. "The woman involved could decide that your actions constituted sexual harassment at any time, or others in the office might feel they were passed over for promotions because you were playing sexual favorites," says Jonathan Levy, a labor-law attorney and CEO of the management-training company Fair Measures. If you are confronted, your best defense is to confess, not deny. "Own up to the truth early, before others have a chance to define it," says crisis-management consultant Helio Fred Garcia. If you come clean, you have a fifty-fifty chance of retaining your job (and some dignity). If you lie and are proven guilty, you're history.

I'm a troll.' As I got older, I worshipped him even more for not taking advantage of a starstruck girl who would have slept with him in a second."

It may seem unfair and even sinister for a woman to put her boss's moral fortitude to the test, but that's where the father-figure stuff comes in. "My dad was in and out of jail," says Karen, who is now close friends with the 47-year-old who showed her the ropes of the banking business 7 years ago. "Jim was the only male role model I'd ever had, and I needed him to be a kind of moral superhero to compensate for my villainous father."

A women who does throw herself at her boss is more likely to be driven by genuine, if misguided, lust than by raw ambition. "When I was in my early 20s, my knee-jerk reaction to a man I admired was to try and sleep with him, because that's the only way I was confident that I could gain his approval," says Hannah, 29, who feels as if she lost out on her chance to learn from a high roller in the movie business. "It wasn't until we were dating that I realized I wanted to be his protégée, not his girlfriend."

Plenty of twenty-something women would never do or say anything inappropriate or unprofessional around their bosses, in or out of work. But since some would and do, it's up to you—the guy with the power—to make sure that conversations and situations don't get out of hand.

DISCOURAGE RUMORS, THEN IGNORE THEM

Sleep with your intern, and people will gossip. Don't sleep with your intern, and people will gossip. So your best strategy is to do all the right things and not waste time or energy stressing over what's being whispered behind your back. Of course, that doesn't mean that you have carte blanche to invite a Rhodes scholar back to your hotel room to go over marketing strategies.

"The key to avoiding suspicion is to interact with a young female assistant in the same ways that you would any other person on her level," says Jonathan Levy, a labor-law attorney and CEO of Fair Measures, a management-training company based in Santa Cruz, California. If you frequently have closed-door meetings or working dinners, or go on business trips with other employees, it won't seem odd to anyone, including a court of law, if they happen with her—as long as her responsibilities and involvement in the work you're doing are appropriate for her position. It might be tempting to invite her to the conference in Maui, but if you don't need her there to get the job done, your co-workers will assume she's fulfilling other duties.

It's natural for you to fixate on the person who shows the most promise, but remember that every member of your staff is hungry for feedback and approval. If the majority of your attention is going to one person, especially a young woman, people will be resentful. And if they're resentful, they're more motivated to paint a picture of you as a lecherous bastard. "I didn't realize I'd been spending an unusual amount of time with my new intern, because she was talented and I was enjoying coaching her. But a co-worker got jealous and sent a 'friendly' e-mail to my girlfriend, warning her that I might be hitting on this girl," says Clinton, a 44-year-old ad agency art director. "I had to explain the situation to the intern and ask her to meet with my girlfriend to assure her that our relationship was purely professional." Telling your female assistant to leave work at the same time as everyone else when you'd both prefer to work together for another hour might be inconvenient, but it's more than worth it if it calls off the dogs.

It's also important to let your intern or assistant know that to win at the corporate game, she has to relate well to others in the office. "Tell her that you think she has more potential than all of them combined, but emphasize the importance of being a team player," says Gallagher. "She should never brag about the access she has to you, your contacts, or high-profile projects—in fact, she should downplay it." Because you've taken an interest in her career, she might have to work twice as hard and be twice as humble to win over the other women in the office, but that's the price she has to pay for special treatment.

You could take precautions like never being seen arriving or leaving events with her, instructing hotels not to give you adjoining rooms, and having other people present at working dinners, but if everything is aboveboard and your company isn't recovering from a scandal or currently on an antiharassment kick, being overly vigilant isn't necessary. The seldom-heard truth is that your career isn't as vulnerable to the effects of gossip as you might think. "If you're already in an upper-management position, unfounded rumors from the company grapevine are inevitable, and the vast majority of men's careers withstand them just fine," says Gallagher. You could say that you're not really at the top of your game until people start trying to bring you down.

MAKE GOOD WITH YOUR WIFE, AND YOURSELF

Of course, the office isn't the only place where speculation can lead to angst. Getting your wife comfortable with the fact that your new protégée at work happens to be a knockout is a lot like defusing a bomb. There's a green wire, a blue wire, and a yellow wire. Cut the wrong one and all hell breaks loose. Which one is that? The one where you come straight out and say that your new assistant is drop-dead gorgeous. "When she comes up in conversation, talk to your wife about the work that she's doing, not her personality or looks," says Dr. Callahan. "If they meet at the office holiday party and your wife comments on how attractive she is, tell her that you're just glad she does her job well." Deflect any attempts your wife might make to get you to admit that you find your assistant easy on the eyes by repeatedly reminding her that she's the one you're married to, she's the one you love, and she's the one to whom you're attracted. Don't assume that she's heard it too many times.

Off the record, if you're secretly smitten with your assistant and it's interfering with your ability to work or just making you feel guilty, this is the time to evaluate your romantic and social life. "You need to pay attention to your personal needs and make sure that you're not trying to satisfy them in the wrong place with the wrong person," says Paul Dobransky, MD, a Chicago psychiatrist and therapist who leads seminars in interpersonal ethics. "Whatever you want from your female employee that extends beyond the realm of business indicates a part of your personal life that's being neglected, whether it's romance, friendship, or just excitement." Plan a romantic weekend with your wife or girlfriend. Reconnect with a friend. Try rock climbing. Or therapy. But if you feel smitten, it means something's wrong; don't look for the answers in your intern's big brown eyes.

And don't be surprised if the prospect of sleeping with your wife, your girlfriend, or any other woman closer to your age and career status doesn't seem quite as hot. The reason is simple: "Power is an aphrodisiac, and you don't have the same power over your significant other," says Dr. Callahan. That's why so many couples invest in fluffy pink handcuffs and satin blindfolds.

BE A MODEL CITIZEN AND STILL HAVE A GOOD TIME

The best possible professional relationship you can have with a talented hottie is one in which you enjoy each other's company, show mutual respect for what the other person brings to the table, and don't take it all too seriously. "It's never a great idea to have power over someone and try to be their buddy, but you don't have to be a robot," says Dr. Dobransky. Be funny, be casual, be open, but don't be intimate. In other words, keep conversation about sex and serious personal issues out of the picture, and not just because it's out of line. "Your assistant or intern may be loyal to you, or she may be aiming to get ahead any way she can," warns Dr. Callahan. "She might repeat the details to other people at work to earn favor."

In the instance when she's the one who comments on the disappointing size of her boyfriend's penis or her raging PMS, shut the topic down gently. Simply changing the subject will send the signal that it's a path you won't go down. If she gets really out of hand, like by informing you she's not wearing any underwear, you have two recommended options: The first is to sit her down and explain that corporate restrictions prevent you from being able to talk about sex with someone who reports to you, so if she wants to keep working together, stuff like that can't happen. The second is to quietly inform HR that they need to call her in for a training course on how to dress and act properly at work. Your point should be that it doesn't matter how much you like each other—for better or worse, you have to follow the rules.

Is flirting allowed? Yes, but keep it subtle. (Caveat: If you don't know what that means, you might want to skip it altogether.) "Flirting with a subordinate can and should be intangible," says Dr. Callahan. "You can give someone a lighthearted look, a smile, that implies you find her attractive in an off-limits kind of way." And as mentioned earlier, as long as other people in the office won't find it unusual, you can invite her out to dinners, parties, and any other events that are work related. Lay off the drinks, and the odds that something forbidden will happen dwindle considerably. "Many sexual harassment cases involve two factors: an off-site location and alcohol," says Levy. "If you're already involved in one, it's a very good idea to avoid the other."

Some men may not be able to handle daily proximity to a babe without letting attraction get in the way, but if you're self-possessed and have a clear idea of what your role in the relationship is, you can sit back and enjoy the fact that your position gives you the opportunity to spend time with a charming young woman—and to know that she's charmed by you.

Be Prepared

What happens when she's had a threesome and you haven't?

BY WILL LEITCH

WE WERE IMPOSSIBLY LATE. The wedding started in 20 minutes, and my girlfriend was still looking over her shoulder into the hotel mirror, examining the proportional ratio between her hips and rear, tousling her hair, drying it, spraying it. Not that I was in a rush. They were her college friends, not mine.

She stripped off one dress and threw on another. I said they both looked great, then turned my attention to the baseball game on TV. Finally, she settled on the blue number with the frills, grabbed her purse, and did one last mirror check. "I just can't believe Helena and Tim are getting married," she said. "Are you nervous to meet them?"

"No. Why?"

"You know," she replied, "because of the threesome?"

The room suddenly became very hot, and the starch in my shirt collar seemed to turn to plaster. It's also possible that the walls began emanating very loud techno music. Threesomes aren't the sort of thing you forget, yet somehow hers had slipped my mind. But now I remembered. Oh, did I.

I sat down on the bed and stared at the television. Apparently some men in bright costumes were playing a game with sticks and balls. "It's no big deal," I managed. "Actually, I'm looking forward to it."

"Good," she said. "My friends will love you. Let's go."

She'd told me years ago about her college threesome. I think she had even told me who was involved. I just hadn't done the math; my imagination hadn't yet marshaled the resources necessary for rendering her, with them, doing whatever sort of bedroom acrobatics they managed to pull off.

That, obviously, was about to change. Whether I liked it or not, I was about to meet two people who have also, I can only presume, brought my girlfriend to orgasm. At the church, wedged in an ergonomically incorrect wooden pew, I tried to entertain myself by checking out the crowd, but inevitably I started making a mental list of

Science of Sex

Risky Business

A new study in the journal *Sexually Transmitted Diseases* reads like a horror show: Half of people visiting a Colorado STD clinic reported condom-use mishaps. Most common: breakage, slippage, and initiation of sex before the condom was put on. Breakage can occur because no space is left at the tip, says Judith Shlay, MD. But the biggest problem: Too many young men (18 to 24) aren't using condoms at all.

36 percent say that if their partner refuses to use a condom, they always refuse to have sex with him or her.

77 percent say it's smart to carry condoms, but only 23 percent always carry them.

51 percent of sexually active young adults always ask their potential partners about STDs before having sex.

46 percent of sexually active men and women "always" or "often" use condoms during sexual activity.

44 percent are not concerned about contracting an STD (39 percent of men, 49 percent of women).

Source: Trojan Condom Survey of sexually active
men and women ages 18 to 24

which guests the happy couple had probably orgied with. At least half of the bridal party, I was sure of that. Oh, and the officiant. And that dude who works at the coffee shop down the street. And the blind guy with the dog. Finally, not a moment too soon, the groom hit the carpet.

He was wearing a low-key tux, glasses, and much facial hair. He looked like the guy you call at work when your computer can't connect to the network. My girlfriend whispered in my ear that he really likes baseball statistics. "You guys would totally get along," she said. That'd be two things we have in common, I guess.

The threesome was never something she tried to hide. On our first date, after listening to my theory on threesomes—if you don't have one by age 30, you never will—she grinned that grin that made me instantly realize she could add something insightful to the discourse. Turns out, while I had a theory, she'd had a threesome. But then she softened the blow: "If we're still together when you turn 30, we might just have to make that happen." Later that night, I sneaked out to enjoy a cellular high five with a friend.

If reality stumbles when you learn that your girlfriend has had a threesome, it falls flat when you come face-to-face with the other parts of her carnal equation. As I watched the groom take his place near the priest/rabbi/guy with a rented Bible, my brain went to three immediate destinations.

1. The last time we were "intimate." It had been a long day, and I'd had a bit to drink. I wasn't at my best. Let's just leave it at that.

2. That porn film from last week. The women's names were Chastity and Sandi. The guy didn't have a name or any body hair—just a penis that could be used for logrolling at the Great Outdoor Games. They lapped at him hungrily.

3. That imaginary place in the brain where I am omnipotent, able
   to see all events, past, present, and future, even events at which
   I was not present. In this place, Sandi is the bride, Chastity is
   my girlfriend, and both of them are lapping Guy with No Body
   Hair hungrily. This is not a fun place for the brain to go.

It was one of those unconventional, nonreligious weddings, and
there was no buildup to the bride's arrival. She just sort of meandered
onto the carpet, sans makeup, wearing pants (pants!) and what looked
like more of a poncho than a wedding dress. It might actually have
been made from deer hides. "She's always had a problem with traditional gender roles," my girlfriend whispered. I saw the bride as a grad
student strumming a guitar, letting her long, blonde hair grow into
thick dreadlocks. I saw her eschewing shoes for an entire summer. I
saw her stripped naked, straddling my girlfriend, while her future
husband...never mind.

In another world, one in which I'm more like Mister Logroller
than Mister Rogers, I might have mustered the balls to turn to my
girlfriend and ask, "Was it miserable? Was it exciting? Was it too good?
Do you wish life was still like it was back then, when you could have
threesomes with your friends and chuckle it off the next day, instead
of dealing with a whimpering boyfriend who complains that it's been
3 days since he's gotten laid?" I gently probed once, but when she
said, ominously, that it was "pretty much" a onetime thing, I stopped.
And the fact is, no matter how ribald the worst-case scenarios in my
head, they're much less terrifying than actually knowing what happened.

The ceremony was very matter-of-fact; it took only about 5 minutes. It was clearly just a formality in the bride and groom's book, an
inconvenience even. Everyone clapped as they left the chapel, and I
noticed that my girlfriend had a single tear rolling down her cheek.

That's when it hit me: They'd all moved on. The happy couple had thank-you letters to write, junk mail to discard, sections of the *New Yorker* to pretend to read—in short, lives to go back to, lives that were moving forward. Like my girlfriend, they didn't think about that threesome anymore, much less talk about it. They'd filed away their own reports on the incident long ago, ones that involved a lot more fumbling and confusion than logrolling and money shots.

But then, what of my girlfriend's promise? My 30th birthday was just 3 weeks away, and a smarter man could certainly parlay being

Blasts from Her Past

What to ask her and what to skip

Ask . . .

"What was your first time like?" It was her sexual coming-out party. "This is usually harmless, sometimes hilarious, and rarely threatening," says sex therapist Gloria Brame, PhD. "Sharing this kind of personal information is a sign of trust."

"What was your biggest blunder?" Her parents walked in. She farted. A cop knocked on the window of the '84 Camaro. Consider these cringe-worthy moments sexual icebreakers. Sex is never perfect, and the easier it is to laugh off the rough edges—past, present, or future—the better sex you'll have with each other.

"What's in your sexual repertoire?" Has she ever watched porn? Tried sex toys? Starred in a home video? Engaged in an all-night, all-nude sorority pillow fight? "What she's done in the past can be a predictor of how you're going to work as a couple," says Dr. Brame.

"What was your wildest night?" "It helps you understand what she's like when she really lets loose," says Carol Rinkleib Ellison, PhD, author of *Women's Sexualities*. One caveat: Keep the sharing about the sex—setting, position, season—not the ex. That way you'll avoid making comparisons.

forced to meet Helena and Tim into the already promised ménage à trois. As we made our way to the reception, I started thinking about my sexual past. Good times, for sure. I'd rate it a 6, maybe a 7, on a scale of 1 to 10. A threesome would bump me to a 9, maybe all the way to a 10. And yet, the prospect wasn't triggering a Pavlovian response. Instead, I started thinking about the complicated logistics. I have this girlfriend, and we have a history, and a future, too. And when I think about our future, I picture a big house and three kids, not her watching me give

"What were your exes like?" "Recognizing what type of sexual baggage a person brings to a relationship will avoid any pressure to create instant intimacy," says Nancy Pina, a relationship expert and the author of *Goodbye, Mr. Wrong.*

Skip . . .

"Who was your best?" Ask her about the longest or thickest she's ever experienced and she just might tell you. And then you'll never sleep right again.

"When was your last one-night stand?" Guess what: She liked to meet people, have fun, and, sure, even mess around once in a while before you met. And so did you. "The less you ask about her random hookups," says Dr. Brame, "the less she'll dig into yours."

"How many partners have you had?" Sex isn't a sport, and she's probably not an all-star. So stay away from statistics. "Just make sure you ask about any STDs she may have been exposed to," says Isadora Alman, a sex therapist and the author of *Doing It: Real People Having Really Good Sex.*

"What happened with those two dudes in college?" Why skip this? Because she had a threesome with those two dudes in college.

oral to a stranger. And what would her father say? Right, he wouldn't have to know. But next month we're going to see a play with her grandparents. How uncomfortable would that be?

No, I don't want a threesome. I just want to have had one.

The reception was lovely. Heartfelt toasts, crying family members, a cake that was taller than anyone not wearing heels. My girlfriend and I made our way to our table and ate that preprocessed wedding food that never quite tastes right. I met old friends, I told harmless ingratiating jokes, and I even danced with a flower girl.

Ultimately, the bride and groom made it over to our table. They were extremely nice people—gregarious, funny, and unassuming. He didn't look like a logroller, her name didn't end with an *i*, and neither looked ready to rev up an orgy at the end of the night. They looked satisfied, exhausted, and very much in love.

The groom shook my hand. "It's a pleasure to meet you, sir," I said.

"You too," he replied. "You are one very lucky guy."

You know, I don't remember much after that.

Am I Normal?

My girlfriend's bad moods put me in a worse mood. Then we're in a funk for days on end.

YES. Moods are contagious. Some professionals believe there are physical changes in your brain and body that occur when you spend time around depressed or negative people. The best way to counteract her negative moods is to make sure you have control of your own. Exercise can help steady the mental seesaw; so can taking capsules of high-quality fish oil, which has been shown to have mood-stabilizing properties. If she's willing, maybe she'll join you.

So, about that 30th birthday. My girlfriend threw me a party at a Mexican restaurant, where a man named Juan gave me flan and a sombrero. We chased margaritas with tequila shots and went home tipsy.

As we walked through the door, I couldn't help but scan the apartment. Empty. Just me and her. She went into the bedroom to change while I grabbed a bottle of champagne. I'd been in this exact place before, in my brain, and had pulled three flutes from the cabinet. But tonight, two seemed just right. "I have a surprise for you, Will," said my girlfriend, emerging. I swung around. "I got you a digital camera! I know how you really wanted one."

I had wanted one. It was a very, very nice digital camera. And so I set the bottle down on the kitchen table, snapped a few pictures of her, took off her clothes, and, for 7 solid minutes, rolled some goddamned logs.

And you know what? It was great. It was fantastic. It was enough.

Make Your Move

IF YOU EARN A LIVING playing hard-bodied heroines in Hollywood blockbusters, you'd better know your way around a leg-press machine. Michelle Rodriguez, 26, has hoisted a few weight stacks in her day, playing a boxer in *Girlfight*, a competitive surfer in *Blue Crush*, and Vin Diesel's sexy, ripped love interest (and fellow car thief) in *The Fast and the Furious*. While she's getting in her reps, Rodriguez studies the mating habits of her fellow gym rats. "I analyze the whole scene when I'm working out," Rodriguez says. "I watch how guys and girls interact. It's really interesting." Her tips on working it while working out:

CHECK YOURSELF. If you're in worse shape than the woman you'd like to approach, rethink the mission. "I think it's hot when people care about themselves," says Rodriguez. "There's a certain level of confidence there that I respect. I'm not talking about perfection, but I wouldn't date somebody more than 20 pounds overweight. It's not healthy, and it's not cute."

READ HER MIND. "Women who want to be approached are easy to spot: They're always smiling and staring at the guys," says Rodriguez. "And they're right there by the dumbbells because that's also where all the mirrors are. They're thinking how good their backsides look in tights," says Rodriguez. "Working out boosts a woman's confidence and her ass." The bad news: Most women—especially if they're good-looking—just want to be left alone. Let spandex be your litmus test.

Meeting Up

Here's how 1,700 men and women met their most recent lovers:

Through an online dating service: **9.9 percent**

Through a friend: **4.5 percent**

In a bar: **12.8 percent**

On the street, passing by: **31 percent**

At a coffee shop: **1.5 percent**

At work: **23.5 percent**

"Women who are serious about the gym don't wear it because, well, it gets wet in all the wrong places."

KEEP IT CASUAL. "When we meet a guy, we know whether we want to jump him," says Rodriguez. "So you've got to have some game. Just don't be a stalker. There's nothing worse than the guy who stares at a woman as he slowly makes his way toward her. Ask if you can work in with her on a machine. Then feel out her attitude. If she's flirting, start a conversation. Or drop a compliment. But be casual about it. Say it and walk away. Otherwise it feels like you want something."

Make Her Yours

IT TAKES MORE than a bouquet and a boom box blaring "In Your Eyes" to hook a woman these days. "Women are so busy; you can't just leave it up to fate that she'll fall for you," says Bonnie Eaker Weil, PhD, author of *Make Up, Don't Break Up.* Your secret strategy: Harness the way her brain creates new memories so you can make yourself unforgettable. Your three-stage plan starts here.

THE HONEYMOON PERIOD: MONTH 1. Emotion turns the brain into a memory sponge. "Pack it with sensory bookmarks," says Dr. Eaker Weil. Take it outside. Forget the candlelit restaurant. "Sweeping settings—deserts, ski resorts, the beach—will stick in her head and stand out from her routine," says Henry Roediger, PhD, a memory researcher at Washington University. Engage her senses. Tastes, sights, smells, and sounds all make a memory easier to recall, says Dr. Roediger. If you're cooking, throw on a new CD and whip up a spicy coconut Thai curry. Play with her. The more active the date, the better it'll stick. Try pottery or rock climbing; both her body and brain will learn something new.

THE MAKE-OR-BREAK PERIOD: MONTH 2. Reinforce the memories you've made and start dropping anchors elsewhere in her life. Revisit the scene. Memories are strengthened by emotion and repetition. Return to the place you first met or take another crack at that Thai curry. "The more you think about something, the more you associate it with your life," says Dr. Roediger. Supply the context. Re-create the ambience with lighting, sounds, and smells. Bring friends. "We're more likely to remember events that have social significance, that other people talk about," says Logan Levkoff, a New York City–based sex educator. Throw a barbecue for her friends. Or invite them all to brunch on a Sunday—and pick up the tab.

THE LONG HAUL: MONTH 3 AND BEYOND. Keep things fresh. Track her tastes. Prove you've been paying attention by skipping the pickles she hates on her sandwich or grabbing a pack of Gummi Bears at the gas station—she loves 'em, remember? "These 'endearing behaviors' are small, but when repeated, they leave an imprint on the brain," says Dr. Eaker Weil. Make anything interesting. "The greatest memories are the least exciting," says Levkoff. Turn a trip to Costco into a free-sample lunch; test-drive a Corvette while your Impala's oil is being changed. Say better good-byes. Your getaways—on business trips or to bachelor parties—cause desire-boosting chemicals to build up in her brain. The more she remembers you, the better the slow burn. Before you hit the road, give her a gift she'll wear, use, or see every day—pajamas, scented bath gel, some fresh flowers—and you'll reap the benefits when you return.

Science of Sex

It's official: New love is like a drug, according to research published in the *Journal of Neurophysiology*. Scientists studied 10 women and 7 men who had recently become infatuated with someone. The participants were shown a photo of their new loves while functional MRI images were taken. The area of the brain that became active (the caudate nucleus and the ventral tegmental area) is the same region associated with reward and motivation. It's also the part that fires up when we satisfy hunger or thirst—or a drug craving. So don't worry—obsession, exhilaration, and anxiety are normal. "We're slaves to passion—to a biological imperative—for a brief time," says Lucy Brown, PhD, a professor of neuroscience at Albert Einstein College of Medicine and one of the study authors. "It's an unconscious motivational-reinforcement system that's activated."

Reveal Your Naked Truths

DE NIRO USED truth serum on Ben Stiller. Your girlfriend has the Internet and a network of gossip-crazed friends. There are few secrets these days. With a phone call or mouse click, she can uncover your dirty laundry—that lost weekend in Cabo; the yacht's worth of credit-card debt. So a preemptive confession may be in order.

"Admitting something wrong/bad/dumb/illegal often provides instant relief," says Greg Fox, author of *Coming Clean: The Best and Worst of DailyConfession.com*. It's also best for her, if done with deft timing and keen judgment. Here's your three-part guide to dredging up the past without driving her away.

TELL HER . . .

"Before speaking up, ask yourself two questions," says Evan Imber-Black, PhD, author of *The Secret Life of Families*. "First, is this relevant information that your mate has a right to know? Second, will spilling it strengthen the relationship and breed intimacy?" Examples: STDs are highly relevant, as are bankruptcies to a couple buying a house. But your brief stint as a Strip-o-Gram deliveryman can stay private. Other mandated disclosures: prison stints and newspaper headlines still lurking on microfiche, ongoing therapy or rehab, failed engagements or marriages, and any live-in lovers you were with for 6 months or more.

> Number of men who've secretly checked the text messages on their partner's phone: **1 in 3**

Come clean when your relationship is on cruise control. "It's ill-advised to tell all during rocky times," says Dr. Imber-Black. Neither tarnish a glow nor deepen a rut. Don't mar a romantic weekend with

He Said/She Said

How should the opposite sex trim down there?

He Said		She Said
6%	Au naturel—let it grow	6%
20%	Maintained, but mostly unfettered	29%
38%	Neatly trimmed, about a quarter-inch long	44%
8%	Artfully trimmed	4%
28%	Completely bare	17%

"Keeping your [pubic] hair trimmed or shaven accentuates your family jewels," says Jamye Waxman, a sex educator and writer for *Playgirl* and PlaygirlTV. "Thinking that you look clean can also enhance how you feel about yourself sexually."

scandalous disclosures, but don't keep planning B&B escapes to put off spilling the beans. "Don't wait so long that the other person whines, 'Why haven't you told me about this before?'" says Katherine Macie, PhD, a behavioral psychologist in Virginia. Examples: An idle Tuesday on the porch after a fight-free month is good. Right before guests arrive for your engagement party, not so good. The best time: right after your mate reveals her most intimate secrets. Of course, when your hand is forced, start talking. If past infidelities are about to be outed by an old mistress or a pending mortgage will snag on a bankruptcy blemish, make sure you're the one to break the news.

LEAVE OUT . . .

Relationships aren't built on squeaky-clean sexual resumes. But beware of how much you share; relationship troubles are often caused by sexual histories, according to Marilyn A. Fithian, PhD, a researcher with the Center for Marital and Sexual Studies in Long Beach, California. That time on the train with your ex, the number of partners you've had, or where you learned that sexual position? Stuff it. "The more specific you are, the easier it is for her to visualize your kinky affairs and the more damage you'll do," says Dr. Fithian. If you must divulge something, keep it general. Otherwise, says Dr. Fithian, "She'll begin to think, 'I'm not adequate. I don't measure up. Where did he learn that?' The less said, the better."

Time Your Moves

AN ALLEY-OOP means nothing if it misses the mark; a bad pass can cost you the game. In hoops and in romance, timing is everything. "You want to meet her needs without her having to ask," says Ava Cadell, PhD. Your playbook:

THE TIP-OFF

RIGHT TIME TO PICK HER UP: AFTER 11 P.M. Late in the evening is "the restless period," says anthropologist David Givens, PhD, author of *Love Signals* and director of the Center for Nonverbal Studies in Spokane, Washington. Wait too long and you'll miss your shot. "The atmosphere becomes less exclusive after 11 o'clock or toward the end of the evening or activity." If her shoulders are turned toward you and she gives you a glance or two, "subconsciously or inadvertently, she has some allegiance to you, even if her attention is zeroed in on another guy," Dr. Givens says.

> Number of men who've snapped X-rated photos on their cell phones: **1 in 4**

THE FAST BREAK

RIGHT TIME TO KISS HER: WHEN SHE'S IN POSITION. You can't throw a no-look pass if your partner isn't expecting the ball. Same with the first kiss, says Dr. Givens. "It's a negotiation, usually based on nonverbal cues, to show that a person's available and to see if the other person is interested." Watch the lips—tight means rejection, Shaq-style. The mouth is "the gatekeeper of the body" and is surrounded by nerve endings, says Rutgers University anthropology professor Helen Fisher, PhD, author of *Why We Love*. If they want to, "women tend to get into a position to let themselves be kissed."

THE SLAM DUNK

RIGHT TIME TO SCORE: BEFORE BRUNCH. "Mornings are often when she's happy and relaxed," says Dr. Fisher. "Most women haven't had anything to drink, and their bodies are more fully awake." Want a selfish reason? You'll be surfing on your highest daily testosterone surge, which means that erection-causing chemicals are more active.

THE FOUL SHOT

RIGHT TIME TO APOLOGIZE: 1 DAY LATER. If you get whistled for a foul, let her take a free throw—listen to her vent. Then take a day and let things cool off before giving your full apology. "The other person needs to know that you've spent a little time thinking about what you've done and why," says Beverly Engel, a marriage and family therapist and the author of *The Power of Apology.*

GAME OVER

RIGHT TIME TO BREAK UP: A DAY BEFORE YOUR—OR HER—BUSINESS TRIP. "Breaking up produces total chaos in the brain," says Dr. Fisher. A forced separation makes the cleanest break. You can minimize the emotional upheaval by breaking up when her job and social life are going well. "When she's embedded in her social network, it will support her through a tough time," Dr. Fisher says.

Rev Her Engine

BUILDING BUZZ WORKS the same whether you're hyping a new car or trying to catch a woman's interest. "When it comes to dating, your 'brand' is crucial for separating yourself from every other man out there," says Logan Levkoff, a New York City–based sexologist and relationship expert. Here's how to convince any woman to take you for a spin.

POSITION YOURSELF. Blend in and you'll be left out. "You must create some sort of product differentiation," says David Newman, a vice president at the advertising giant Grey Worldwide. Stand out, but subtly. A cowboy hat and sleeveless T-shirt will get you the wrong kind of attention. "Minor differences are appealing," says anthropologist David Givens, PhD, author of *Love Signals* and director of the Center for Nonverbal Studies in Spokane, Washington. Is everyone wearing striped shirts? Try a pearl-snap button-down. Now, work on perfecting your pitch. Your first moments with someone are like a commercial. "For most people, chemistry is instantaneous. So make sure you use those first few minutes wisely," says Levkoff. Show you have the conversational jujitsu to draw out her most interesting interests and desires, and offer up some of your own to match.

BUILD BUZZ. Chrysler copped some of Snoop Dogg's cool by developing a TV ad with the rapper and Lee Iacocca. So choose your wingmen wisely. The "glitter effect"—you appear more attractive when you're around attractive people—can boost your prospects with some women, but tact matters more. "Surround yourself with 'players' and you might be considered one, too," says Levkoff. You'll also need to restrict supply. Don't speed home with the easiest girl in the bar. "The more selective you seem," says Dr. Givens, "the higher your market value will rise." Build word of mouth. Billboards can be trumped by grassroots marketing. Win over her friends and you'll be halfway to winning her over. "Once you've built that buzz, people go crazy," says Newman.

BRANCH OUT. Want to build brand lust? "You have to keep people emotionally engaged," says Andy Lindblade, a strategic planner for the ultracreative ad agency Wieden + Kennedy, whose clients include ESPN and Nike. Tweak your look. Apple updates the look of its iPod to keep things fresh. You do the same. "It could be as subtle as a small change in wardrobe," says Levkoff. "You don't want to change too much; it's important to stay confident in your style." Just develop new features. "You always need to have a new story to tell," says Lindblade. Whether it's a product or a guy at a bar, "people are looking for fresh reasons to check something out."

On the Dating Scene

64 percent of men simply want more dates.

37 percent want more booty calls.

27 percent would like a more "open" relationship with their partner.

15 percent want to stop screwing around and make the move to monogamy.

Win Her on V Day

PHINEAS MOLLOD AND JASON TESAURO, authors of *The Modern Lover*, offer these tips to make this Valentine's Day the best ever.

ROSES ARE WRONG. Roses once a year means the calendar, and not romance, motivates you. Offer something unique, like a bunch of wildflowers or a houseplant that will last all year.

CARDS CAN KILL. Women sniff out drugstore cards from 20 paces. Homemade is better. Use construction paper to make old-school valentines, then stick them in her path. She'll be giddy as a schoolgirl.

DINNER IS DULL. A romantic evening shouldn't include a restaurant crammed full of other couples. Use the home-field advantage and serve her a meal of finger foods—mini-quiches, egg rolls, or sushi, followed by chocolate-dipped fruits. She'll be eating out of your hand all night.

ASK THE GIRL NEXT DOOR

The honest truth about women from our lovely neighbor

Which is better: asking for a woman's number or giving her mine?
Asking for her digits is the default action when it's clear that a woman is interested. But if you have a feeling she's on the fence, hand her your card and say that you hope she'll drop you an e-mail sometime. That way, you don't risk rejection or make an undecided girl feel pressured. She'll find your card in her purse the next day, glance at it over the course of the week, and perhaps finally conclude that you were pretty cute after all.

Is there a way to ask out a hot girl at church without her thinking I'm the guy who goes to church to pick up women?
What's so bad about a man looking for a date at church? It's a lot sweeter than scoping out chicks at a bar—and smarter, too, since you'll already have something significant in common. Just confess that you're embarrassed about asking a girl out at church, but the prospect of getting to know her is worth the humiliation. That approach is honest and humble, two characteristics that are bound to win over a God-fearing girl—or, really, any woman.

My girlfriend wants to know what I'm doing for every holiday weeks in advance. What's the deal with women and holidays?
Uh, I do that, too. Look, half the reason we give guys a hard time is because we're getting it on the other end. Starting in early November, my mother will call me up once a week, wanting to know what I'm doing for Thanksgiving and Christmas. I want her off my back, so I start bugging my boyfriend about it. The other half is because we want to buy new dresses and wear them someplace fancy, damn it, and no boyfriend or husband or anyone else is going to get in our way.

My girlfriend is going to Vegas for a girls' weekend. Should I worry?

Don't sweat it. Your girlfriend will put on a very short dress, go to a dark club, and get drunk. But she won't cheat on you. Girls are funny that way. When we're in a group, we're far more interested in each other's company than in that of men. And we're insanely protective. If, in a cosmo-induced haze, your girlfriend were to let a strange guy get too close, her friends would flock around her within seconds. (Oh, and she might take in a male strip review, but they're about as erotic as an episode of *Reno 911!*)

Should You Shack Up?

BEFORE YOU TURN THE occasional sleepover into a full-time love-in, know the score.

1. Why do you want to move in?
a. It's the next logical step.
b. She lives near a great pizza joint.
c. She threatened to dump me.

"Don't drift into a cohabiting relationship," says Andrew Cherlin, PhD, author of *The Deinstitutionalization of American Marriage.* "Moving in without a plan is a recipe for disaster."

2. Why does she want to do this?
a. I'm a vital part of her life.
b. So we can pick baby names.
c. A ton of her stuff needs fixing.

"Women are taught that men may think, 'Why buy the cow when you can get the milk for free?'" says Logan Levkoff, PhD, a New York City–based sex educator. "Men must factor that into any promises they make."

3. You started discussing this . . .
a. About 6 months ago.
b. Last week, during *Lost.*
c. I left a note: "See ya Friday."

There's no white dress or unity candle, but moving in together is a big deal. "This should be a relationship that's going somewhere," Levkoff says. "If you're not truly committed to a future with this person, that's a red flag saying you shouldn't do it."

4. What do your parents think?
a. They're really happy for us.
b. Eventually, they'll deal.
c. Shhh! They don't know.

Living together can be a minefield, especially if religion is a factor. Wynne Whitman, coauthor of *Shacking Up*, says one woman who kept it a secret felt "a lot of guilt, and it upset her boyfriend, too. He wondered why she wouldn't tell her parents."

5. How will you handle expenses?
a. It's detailed in our contract.
b. We'll figure it out as we go.
c. "I got this. You get it next time."

"If you fail to lay it out in the beginning, you'll resent each other in the end," says David Bach, author of *Smart Couples Finish Rich*. "Be clear about what's shared and what's separate"—starting with the joint checking account.

SCORING

Each A answer, 3 points; B, 2 points; C, 1 point

12–15 POINTS: You're the perfect boyfriend and roomie.

8–11 POINTS: You probably won't end up on *Jerry Springer*.

5–7 POINTS: Some people—you—are better off alone.

SEX SECRETS

With the help of *Cosmopolitan* magazine, we asked 6,000 men and women about sex. Our findings: Both men *and* women want sex equally as often. In fact, 35 percent of us—both men and women— want sex two or three times a week. If that doesn't sound like what's going on in *your* life, read on. From 13 ways to spice up your sex life, to 10 sexy spots on her body that'll get her going with just a touch, to 5 moves to make her happy in record time, we hope this section will help you to uncover the secrets to great sex under your own covers.

13 Ways to Spice Up Your Sex Life

1. Drop this bomb: "You remember the time we [insert personal-best sex saga here]? I bet we could do even better."

2. Maul her for 10 seconds when she least expects it. A mini-maul here, a mini-maul there. Next thing you know, you'll have a strip-maul.

3. After your next screaming match, right before the makeup sex, don't bother with the "I love you" cliché. Just tell her, "You know, you're the only person I'd ever tolerate talking to me like that. You're that amazing."

4. No screaming matches lately? Have one, fast. If she's screaming at you, she still gives a damn. Silence from a woman means something has died. (Or will die. Tonight. In his sleep.)

5. Imagine what life would be like single—nights on the town, drop-of-a-hat vacations, those long-put-off season tickets. Enjoy that right now. With a built-in date. So pick something fun and do it.

6. Learn a new sport together—like golf or fencing—that encourages you to admire each other's form.

7. Go Gomez Addams on her. Speak Spanish. Dance the Mamushka. Kiss her from her wrist to her armpit. Blow up a train set together. Cara mia!

8. Commit an unsolicited act of cleanliness.

9. This weekend, take her to the grocery store to buy ingredients for a great dinner. Also pick up food specifically ear-
   marked as body paint.

10. You're both 10 excess pounds away from feeling good about
    yourselves again. Drop 'em together. It'll be you and her
    against the world, just like old times.

11. You haven't offered up a late-night postcoital confession in a
    very long time. Surprise her.

12. Reinstate one courtesy toward her that's been lost since your
    courtship: opening the car door for her, bringing her flowers,
    holding in your gas.

13. Organize a cheesy diamond-commercial moment—like
    reproposing to her at Trafalgar Square in front of family.
    Overwrought? Yeah, but do the math: jewelry + effort +
    pigeons + her parents = months of rough sex.

Start Her Engine

Arousal for men is simple. For the 2,143 women we surveyed, however, it's a matter of relaxation and release

BY MATT BEAN

HERE'S A GUIDE to her pleasure, and yours.

THAT FACE. A woman's brain shuts down for orgasm. Commence the shutdown sequence by holding her head in your lap and massaging the area above her eyebrows with your thumbs. "People carry a lot of tension in the face, and this helps them release and become more receptive to arousal," says anthropologist David Givens, PhD, author of *Love Signals* and director of the Center for Nonverbal Studies in Spokane, Washington. Look for her lips to part, he says: "When a person is aroused, he or she will relax the muscles that keep the jaw shut."

THOSE EARS. These are portals to two forms of arousal: physical (reflexogenic) and mental (psychogenic), says Emily Nagoski, PhD, a sex researcher at Indiana University. Touch or massage the rim of her ear between your thumb and forefinger while cradling the back of her head with your fingers. (Ignore the insensitive earlobe.) As she responds, graze the ridge of her outer ear with the tip of your nose, says Anne Hooper, coauthor of *269 Amazing Sex Tips and Tricks for Men*. "Just hearing you breathe will turn her on," she says.

THAT NECK. Brush your lips between her throat and chin, says Sandor Gardos, PhD, founder of Mypleasure.com. "The skin is thinner where the body flexes. The nerves and blood vessels are closer to the surface—that's why it's also a perfume point." You'll engage sensory receptors and trigger an emotional response. "It feels very intimate to let a person that close," says Debby Herbenick, PhD, a sex researcher with the Kinsey Institute, in Indiana.

THOSE LIPS. Kissing is your entrance exam for the rest of her body. "It tells her that you understand how to be subtle, no matter where you are on her body," says Hooper. You're also giving her a hormonal hors d'oeuvre, flooding her hypothalamus (the brain's arousal center) with pheromone-laden smells and tastes. Softly lick her upper lip or tug it gently between your lips. Deep red lips indicate arousal.

HER FINGERS. During a movie or long flight, tease her palm; hands are dense with sensory receptors. Spread your fingers outward from the upper part of her palm, slowly moving them up her fingers. Do it lightly—touch sensitive receptors in the skin respond better than the pressure-sensitive receptors inside (whose job is grabbing). "It's discreet enough for no one to notice, but enticing enough to awaken other parts of her body," says Lauren Slade, founder of the Universal College of Reflexology.

HER FOREARMS. "The inner part of the wrist is extremely sensitive to temperature," says Dr. Herbenick. Try licking her wrist and blowing softly to create a cooling sensation; special receptors there are tuned to detect differences in temperature. (It's the site that moms and dads use to check heated baby formula.) And there are sensitive receptors in hair follicles: "Any area with fine, downy hair is going to respond best to a light, almost nonexistent touch," says Gardos. "Just stimulate the hairs and you'll give her shivers."

THOSE BREASTS. Pay respects to the nerve-rich erogenous tissue at the top and underside of the breast before touching the nipple. "Your technique should be so light that it barely indents the skin," says Kerrie Grow McLean, a sex therapist at the Berman Center, in Chicago. The nipple (which, like the clitoris, feeds into orgasm-inducing neurons in the brain) contains receptors called Meissner's corpuscles, cells that adjust to varied stimuli, like the friction of a shirt or the moisture of a tongue. The longer you tease around the nipple, the more intense direct stimulation will be.

> Percentage of women who climax during oral sex: **42**

THE BACK OF HER KNEES. Many women find this spot ticklish at first. Just wait. "She probably is not aroused enough," says Dr. Gardos. Work on erogenous zones first. Cover the entire back of her leg, then trace your fingers down her thigh and calf and graze the back of her knee, using the full length of three fingers. A firmer touch can stimulate the pressure-sensitive nerve endings, or Pacini's corpuscles, in the skin as well, taking away the tickle.

HER BACK. Knead the muscles between her shoulder blades and spine, and follow with light fingertip strokes. "As you get lower and lower down the back, the nerves become more sensitive," says Dr. Gardos. Let your fingers drift to her sides, gently touching the sides of her breasts. During sex, take a back-rub break to delay ejaculation. "Switching to a back rub is like, 'Wow, he's caring and considerate and not just all about sex,'" Dr. Herbenick says. "Little does she know he's also using the technique to last longer."

THOSE LEGS. Dutch researchers found that the mere expectation of touch triggers activity in the planning and motivation centers of the brain, crucial for building arousal. "Women want to wonder, 'What is he going to do next?'" says Dr. Herbenick. "That mindset is crucial for psychological arousal and orgasm." Stroke her thighs in the direction of her vagina, but pull away before you reach it. Breathe on her or brush your fingers very close, awakening the skin, Dr. Gardos says. "This will transmit a very different sort of sensation than if you're actually making contact."

Be a Much Better Lover

9 ways to go from *what?* to *wow!*

EVERYTHING YOU NEED to know about sex you learned in the backseat of a Mustang in 1982. But as a grown-up, you know that making love happens all day. A great lover can please her in bed and out. Here's how to . . .

GET SWEATY WITH HER. A 10-year study of 168 couples by researchers at the University of Texas found that men and women who work out together as a couple have more satisfying sex. Choose noncompetitive sports, such as hiking, road biking, running, and skiing, suggests Megan Babkes, PhD, a professor of social psychology of sport and physical activity at the University of Northern Colorado.

> Minutes it takes the average woman to reach orgasm: **27**

INSTANTLY IMPROVE YOUR RELATIONSHIP. Turn off the game. Listen to her. Repeat what she said. Tell her that what she said makes sense.

REMEMBER THIS RULE. Your wife's happiness (and subsequently yours) is directly proportional to the number of times a day you call her.

TEACH HER TO SIGNAL FOR SEX. Because women are better communicators in general, we assume they're good at communicating in the bedroom.

Not so. She may be in the mood for something special but too shy or proper to speak its name. The next time the two of you are getting playful, ask her to help you come up with a secret code word or phrase for a certain sexual act. (Example: "Honey, tonight let's do the...")

BUY THE RIGHT LINGERIE. Lingerie, when given as a gift, should stand out from what she wears every day, but not so much that she feels embarrassed wearing it. "If she doesn't feel comfortable, you'll never see it. But if she does feel comfortable and sexy, she'll be proud to show you her wares," says Rebecca Apsan, owner of La Petite Coquette (www.thelittleflirt.com), in New York City. A chemise (a thin slip or short, slinky French nightgown) is a safe bet on both accounts. Because it's loose fitting, it will flatter her figure no matter what her body type—a feat that's difficult to accomplish with more complicated panty sets.

> Minutes it takes the average man: **11**

MAKE UP. You forgot her birthday. Immediately make reservations at her favorite restaurant. "Tell her, for example, that you knew her birthday was on Wednesday but that you wanted to take her out on Saturday," says Tina B. Tessina, PhD, author of *The Unofficial Guide to Dating Again*. If she nailed your forgetfulness, however, the only option is to apologize profusely. Send a handwritten note and flowers to her workplace (that's key) so her friends notice. "Flowers heal almost anything," says Dr. Tessina. Follow with a romantic gift.

GIVE A BETTER MASSAGE. "Think of massage as a theatrical experience," says Gordon Inkeles, author of *The Art of Sensual Massage*. Dim the lights, play soft music, and warm the bedsheets (throw them in the dryer for a couple of minutes beforehand).

1. **GREASE YOUR PALMS.** Light vegetable oils, such as safflower, scented with a few drops of lemon juice work just as well as expensive massage oils. Pour about 2 tablespoons into the palms of your hands and rub them together to warm the oil.

2. **KNEAD HER.** Place one open hand over the other and begin making small circles across her neck and shoulders (that's where women carry most of their tension). Apply even pressure from

your fingertips to the base of your palm. "Be generous," Inkeles says. "Don't limit a stroke to two or three repetitions. If you get those nice sighs of recognition, do 20 or 30 repetitions of the same stroke."

3. **TOUCH HER IN WAVES.** When you're stroking your partner, don't move up and down her body in straight lines. If you move your hands in a wavy, irregular pattern, the nerves in her skin are surprised by your touch, and they become more excited.

4. **HYPNOTIZE YOUR MOTHER-IN-LAW.** She's still frosty, and a family get-together is coming up. Instead of avoiding her, engage her in conversation and talk with your hands at waist to midchest

A Gentleman Knows . . .

How to help a woman on with her coat: Stand behind her and to her right with the jacket just below her shoulder. Let her raise her arm, but guide the sleeve to her hand rather than have her flail and become ensnared. Once her arm is safely through, slide the jacket across her back and repeat on the port side, says Peter Post, author of *Essential Manners for Men*.

A little classical music: Despite your best efforts to avoid it, you know some opera and classical music already: Bizet's *Carmen* (*The Bad News Bears*), Rossini's *The Barber of Seville* (*Bugs Bunny*), Ravel's *Boléro* (Bo Derek). When listening to opera, remember that it's essentially a guy talking about problems with a woman, says Scott Speck, music director of the Mobile Symphony and the Washington Ballet. Play the bartender and see if you can decipher the problem. If you go to a performance, buy balcony seats. They're cheaper, and the sound is better there.

How to say thanks: The note is brief and handwritten in black ink on a personalized note card.

level—a confident yet nonconfrontational posture, says Tom
Nicoli, a board-certified hypnotist and the author of A *Better
You by Hypnosis*. When you're alone, say in a friendly tone, "I
know we got off on the wrong foot. Whatever happens, I want
you to know that I love your daughter. I also know that you and
I would like to get along, and [pause] I know that we will." The
pause wakes up her subconscious as you implant this positive
suggestion. You're being sincere while subtly telling her that
you're not going anywhere. You may never win her over, but
you will make allies with the rest of the family by trying to
thaw out Madame Ice.

Mix It Up

5 moves to make her happy in record time

THE DOWNWARD DOG

THE PURPOSE: Allows for deeper thrusts

HOW IT WORKS: She's facedown on the bed, hips raised

THE BENEFIT: This position creates a snug fit, "making you feel larger," says Rebecca Rosenblat, a sex therapist and the author of *Seducing Your Man*. It also puts pressure on the hard-to-reach pleasure zones just behind her vagina. To last longer, try "shallow thrusting and deep breathing," advises April Masini, author of *Date Out of Your League*. "Exhale with each thrust."

HINT: Don't be a battering ram. "Move your hips from side to side, too," says Diana Wiley, PhD, a sex therapist.

THE FACE-OFF

THE PURPOSE: Makes height differences disappear

HOW IT WORKS: You sit on a chair or the edge of a bed, she faces you on your lap.

THE BENEFIT: Greater flexibility. "She can easily control the angle and depth of entry," says Dr. Wiley, "and this is a good way for a man to learn what sort of rhythm his partner prefers." Sitting is also great for marathon lovemaking because "no one has to worry about their legs or arms giving out on them," says Rosenblat.

HINT: Your hands can roam; take advantage of the 8,000 nerves of the clitoris—or the millions elsewhere on her body.

THE PRETZEL

THE PURPOSE: Blends the doggy and missionary styles

HOW IT WORKS: She lies on her left side. You kneel between her legs, curling her right leg around your right side and straddling her left leg. Use your hands to bring her toward you.

THE BENEFIT: The deeper penetration of doggy-style sex, without the loss of face-to-face contact. Also, ergonomics: "A lot of women can't stand doggy-style, because it hurts their backs," says Rosenblat.

HINT: Add manual stimulation. Your right arm is perfectly positioned to tuck under her right leg to lend a helping hand.

THE SHOULDER HOLDER

THE PURPOSE: Targets her G-spot, makes you feel bigger

HOW IT WORKS: She rests both legs on one of your shoulders.

THE BENEFIT: "Any position in which a woman raises her legs narrows the vagina," says Rosenblat. Slide her feet down to your chest, one foot on each of your pectoral muscles, and start her in a rocking side-to-side or up-and-down motion. She's in a perfect position to control how you stimulate her G-spot.

HINT: Keep your sensors tuned: "If she's pushing a body part into you, she digs the position," Rosenblat says. "If she's pulling back, try something else."

THE COWGIRL'S HELPER

THE PURPOSE: Puts her in control, lets you lend a helping hand

HOW IT WORKS: She squats on top, raising and lowering herself with her thighs. You support her by holding her hips and rising to meet each thrust.

THE BENEFIT: She'll appreciate your ceding the sexual remote control. "This move allows her to

> Percentage of women who always climax on top: **23**

choose between shallow and deep thrusting," says Rosenblat. "Shallow will stimulate the front third of her vagina, the most sensitive part."

HINT: It takes strong thighs for her to maintain this position, so use your arms to help assume some of the heavy lifting.

Eat for a Sexier Life

Food really can put you in the mood. Here's how

BY DENISE FOLEY

CUPID DOESN'T ALWAYS USE AN ARROW; sometimes he uses a fork. And though the National Library of Medicine isn't exactly teeming with studies on edible aphrodisiacs—foods that are arousing—if you've ever been fed a lemon-drenched raw oyster by the object of your desire, you know there must be something there.

Aphrodisiacs derive their name from the Greek goddess of sexual rapture, Aphrodite, the mother of our little archer of love. And, as most science types will tell you, that's not where the mythology stops. The paltry research that does exist on love potions has built on original hypotheses thousands of years old, like those of first-century Roman philosopher and physician Pliny the Elder, who believed that the blood of a bat, collected on wool and placed under the head of a woman, would make her lusty. (Pliny was also a big fan of tongue of goose "taken in either food or drink," but mercifully this research has gone unfunded.)

Of course, you can't expect that quaffing an oyster will work with the alacrity of, say, Viagra, which fixes a guy's plumbing in 14 minutes to a half hour. However sensual creamy dark chocolate feels in your mouth, it isn't going to go directly to your brain, dim the lights, and start playing Barry White. Nonetheless, research suggests that the ancients might have been on to something; some of the classic aphrodisiacs actually contain nutrients critical to sexual function. And if you're convinced of the powers of artfully applied marshmallow whip, that's just fine: University of Michigan researchers recently discovered that a placebo—a sham treatment—triggers the brain to produce its own opioids to ease pain. If we can be tricked into producing our own analgesia, why not our own Spanish fly?

THE LOOK OF LOVE

When the ancients developed their love potion theories, they relied heavily on food porn: Whatever resembled genitalia was ipso facto the recipe for desire. So, there are the symbolically phallic foods: asparagus, carrots, bananas, and avocados (fruits of what the Aztecs called the "testicle tree"). Among the Chinese, powdered rhino horn gets its mojo from its resemblance to an erect penis, although the deflating truth is that it's nothing more than keratin, the raw material also in our fingernails. On the feminine side, there are vulvalike oysters and ovarylike figs, peaches, pomegranates (also called "love apples"), and, of course, eggs. The good news is that at least some of these foods are full of vitamins, minerals, and steroids that can help keep sex organs running smoothly and hormones flowing like champagne at a wedding reception.

Among edible aphrodisiacs, the modest bivalve mollusk is undoubtedly king. Just six oysters supply 43 milligrams of zinc, the mineral that plays a pivotal role in sexual maturation. Without it, you'd be permanently prepubescent. Thank zinc for helping your body produce testosterone, a hormone that can drive desire in both men and women. Oysters are also high in dopamine, the so-called pleasure chemical of the brain. A team of American and Italian researchers found that bivalve mollusks such as oysters, clams, and mussels are chock-full of amino acids that increase levels of the sex hormones testosterone and progesterone, at least in lab rats.

Then there's asparagus, which contains more steroids than the average pro wrestler. "These steroids—mostly phytoestrogens—can act like a blast of hormone therapy," says Washington, DC–based herb expert Douglas Schar, author of *The Backyard Medicine Chest: An*

Herbal Primer. "They can really get you going." There is some evidence that phytoestrogens can boost the level of testosterone circulating in your body; they seem to stop the hormone from converting to a form that's associated with male-pattern baldness (but not libido). Plus, under the right conditions, asparagus can grow 10 inches in 24 hours, and if that doesn't convince you, nothing will.

ONE SINGULAR SCENTSATION

A line of aphrodisiac research that passes the sniff test involves our sense of smell, and it may help explain why the romantic dinner has become part of the human courtship display.

Animals have a set of receptor cells in their noses that can pick up chemical signals from potential mates and transmit them like suggestive e-mails to the areas of the brain that control reproduction. One whiff of a female mouse and a passing male is hot to trot. Human sensory cells may differ from animals', but we still pick up the sex scents called pheromones. "Humans do have a very well-endowed olfactory system, and it's through this system that pheromones are likely processed," says Charles Wysocki, PhD, a neuroscientist at the Monell Chemical Senses Center in Philadelphia. Your nose, he explains, "is an interstate highway to your brain, specifically the parts of the brain that regulate mood, emotions, and reproduction." That makes it, at least unofficially, a sex organ.

In previous research, Alan Hirsch, MD, neurological director of the Smell and Taste Treatment and Research Foundation in Chicago, found that many patients who had lost their senses of smell also lost interest in sex. That piqued his curiosity about the power of scents to boost desire. To see what, if any, aromas could provoke a sexual response, he asked a group of 30 women to sit in a lab, attached to a device that measures vaginal blood flow, and sniff 30 different odors, ranging from licorice (a folkloric aphrodisiac) to cheese pizza (a cheap date). Since turnabout is fair play, he asked a group of 31 men to sit in a laboratory, their penises attached to a machine that measures blood flow, and sniff the same 30 odors.

What he found: The men responded sexually (with increased penile blood flow) to all of the aromas, proving the theory that it doesn't take much. But the hands-down winner for most arousing smell—it increased penile blood flow by 40 percent—was the mingled scents of pumpkin pie and lavender. Runners-up were doughnuts with black licorice (32 percent) and pumpkin pie with doughnuts (20 percent). Women weren't as turned on by scents, which surprised Dr. Hirsch because they tend to have keener noses. But the combined aromas of cucumber and Good & Plenty candy (which is licorice scented) and the scent of baby powder tied for first place (a 13 percent increase in vaginal blood flow). Pumpkin pie plus lavender followed, with an 11 percent increase.

You may not be ready to dab pumpkin pie behind your ears, but Dr. Hirsch's work at least gives you ideas about desserts for seduction. Dr. Wysocki advises experimentation. "Oysters aren't the only food that people find stimulating." (Guys, a word to the wise: In Dr. Hirsch's study, three scents actually turned women off: cherries, barbecued meat, and men's cologne. "My advice to men would be throw away the cologne and get some Good & Plenty," says Dr. Hirsch.)

WHEN IT JUST FEELS GOOD

Some aphrodisiacs' effects on the body may mimic aspects of carnal pleasure. For example, the capsaicin in chile peppers and the organosulfur compounds in garlic can make you hot, hot, hot—temperature-wise—largely by improving blood flow. And the caffeine in coffee and chocolate is a stimulant that may produce a rise in both blood pressure and endorphins, hormones that can make you feel "high." You might say chocolate is a treasure trove of pleasurable ingredients. Its alkaloid methylxanthines have been shown to cross the blood-brain barrier, and once there, at least theoretically trigger those wonderful arousal sensations. Chocolate also contains arginine, an amino acid the body converts to nitric oxide (NO). At least for men, NO can become YES: The erectile dysfunction pill Viagra works by increasing NO in the body, which opens up blood vessels in the penis. There are two other potential sex drugs in that naughty Whitman's Sampler: Anandamide, one of the brain's messenger molecules, derives its name from the Sanskrit word for bliss. It can trigger the same sense of well-being that you get from marijuana (cannabis);

Play with Your Food

Here's what the experts advise for some romantic food play:

Create your own menu. You think oysters are a turn-on; your partner would rather chug Drano than raw shellfish. Don't be bound by tradition. "Find out what your partner likes; don't just guess," says sex counselor and researcher Beverly Whipple, PhD, a professor emerita at Rutgers University and coauthor of The G Spot: And Other Discoveries About Human Sexuality. "You don't want to get that wrong." You can find some help—and some recipes—from cookbooks such as Booty Food by the Food Network's sex symbol, Jacqui Malouf, or Intercourses: An Aphrodisiac Cookbook by Martha Hopkins and Randall Lockridge.

Cook for one another. What's nurturing can also be sexy, says Malouf. Her husband, she says, "wooed me with food." When he invited her to his place for dinner, he was making fettuccine noodles from scratch. "He rolled out the dough in front of me, taught me how to cut it, and showed me how to make his grandmother's tomato butter sauce. It was so intimate, such a window into him and how he moves through life, that I knew right away this was the guy."

Don't forget presentation. Not all food requires a table setting. "Turn it even targets cannabinoid receptors in the brain. And phenylethyl-amine (PEA) is a mood regulator that contributes to chocolate's amphetamine-like effects and may stimulate production of the arousal chemical dopamine.

Just as there are chocoholics, there are chocoskeptics. Even the International Cocoa Organization doubts that enough PEA reaches the brain to do much of anything (do they not eat the stuff themselves?). But chocolate—as both a dessert and a body paint—is

your lover into dessert with chocolate sauce or Jell-O or ripe mango—and lick it off," suggests sexologist Ava Cadell, PhD, EdD.

Engage all your senses. Taste is important, but so are aroma and touch, and a little mood music wouldn't hurt either. "People are such head-dwellers that whatever you can do to get them into their bodies makes sex better," says herb expert Douglas Schar. "A switch flips in their brains, and they shift out of intellect and into horn dog." Try some Moroccan food. Fragrant with exotic spices and eaten with the fingers, it will indulge many of your senses and possibly rock your casbah.

You be Lady, he'll be the Tramp. When we reached Dr. Cadell, she was wrapping up filming for a TV series she's starring in called *The Science of Sex*, to be released in the United Kingdom. "Today we shot two lovers eating a stalk of asparagus," she explained. "The woman started on one end, the man at the other, and they met in the middle. That's a very, very sexy thing to do."

By now, it should be clear that you don't really need scientific studies to prove that food is edible erotica. You just need an adventurous spirit and a little spreadable chocolate. "The FDA would call aphrodisiacs a lot of bunk," says Malouf. "But I've never wanted to date anyone who worked for the FDA."

inextricably linked to romance, so don't be too hasty about kicking it out of bed until all the evidence is in.

In fact, simply maintaining faith in your favorite aphrodisiacs may accord them power. In an online survey of more than 400 people, about 40 percent said eating certain foods made them hungry for sex afterward, and they had some clear ideas about what did it for them, says Linda DeVillers, PhD, a Marina del Rey, California, sex therapist who conducted the poll. "The top five aphrodisiacs, in order, are chocolate, strawberries, ice cream, pasta, and whipped cream.

He Said/She Said

What is the key factor in deciding whether to sleep with a new partner?

He Said		She Said
26%	His or her body	3%
17%	The passion (how hot things get)	15%
4%	Whether it's "too soon"	9%
26%	Where the relationship is headed	46%
27%	Other (goatee, salsa skills, etc.)	27%

Women gauge whether a relationship is "going somewhere" (including the bedroom) by how well you understand them, says Mark Elliott, PhD, director of the Institute for Psychological and Sexual Health in Columbus, Ohio. Meeting her for the first time? Let the talk, not the hooch, flow freely. Then act on her hints: Planning a night out? Don't book a four-star meal if she said she likes burgers at the beach, for example. "You have to make her feel special using any inferences you have," Dr. Elliott says. Extra credit: Plan a date she'll love but she knows you'll hate.

And about 65 percent of the respondents said that among drinks, champagne is their personal favorite."

So what do those foods have in common? That's right—good times. They remind us of birthday parties, Valentine's Day, and movie romance. Who could forget the sexy supper scene in *Lady and the Tramp* as the mutt hero and purebred heroine slurp the same strand of spaghetti? Or *9½ Weeks,* in which whipped cream undergoes its big-screen transformation from dessert topping to sexual aid? But it's also possible that you find Reddi-wip sexy because it recalls the cumulus of cream and sugar on top of Mom's rice pudding. "It's simple," says Dr. DeVillers. "The foods that give us pleasure turn us on."

This means that if the only scientific theory that proves that aphrodisiacs work is the placebo effect, you're in luck. Thanks to your memory-stocked mind, the placebo effect can turn even a tuna casserole into a love potion. "After all," says Los Angeles clinical sexologist Ava Cadell, PhD, EdD, "the brain is the greatest aphrodisiac of all."

Find Satisfaction

MOANS MEAN YOU'RE headed in the right direction. But aural clues aren't enough. "You don't even have to ask what she wants if you just read her body the right way," says Joan Elizabeth Lloyd, author of *The Perfect Orgasm*. Translate easily with this Rosetta stone.

CATCH HER EYE. "When women aren't pleased—in or out of the bedroom—they minimize eye contact," says psychologist Lorel Lindstrom, PhD. Test her by dropping a compliment—"You taste delicious"—and watching her eyes. If she returns your gaze and the sex heats up, you're on track.

RETURN THE FAVOR. A woman will mirror your moves if she likes them, or "project," touching or kissing you how (or where) she wants attention. Take note of what she's initiating. "Women usually won't do things to you that they don't want done to themselves," Lloyd says.

DON'T ASK. Her body will tell you whether she's satisfied. "A woman can't fake the involuntary muscle spasms that occur in her vagina during orgasm," says sexologist Ava Cadell, PhD, EdD. They're often hard to detect, so look for her nipples, labia, and clitoris to swell and darken.

FOLLOW HER HIPS. "They're an indicator that she's aroused," says Lloyd. The cadence of her writhing can act as your metronome, telling you how hard and how fast to stimulate her.

Win the Sack Race

SEX IS LIKE RUNNING. Jog the 100-yard dash and you'll come in last; sprint through the first mile of a marathon and you'll go limp sooner or later. "You really have to pace yourself," says Beverly Whipple, PhD, coauthor of the *G-Spot: And Other Discoveries About Human Sexuality.* "Otherwise, everybody loses." Here's how to make the most of the time you have.

YOU HAVE 5 MINUTES

YOUR STRATEGY: SKIP THE SCHEDULE. She loves quickies for the spontaneity. You love them because they're like *SportsCenter*: all highlight, no filler. Take her lead, says Tara Roth Madden, author of *Romance on the Run.* "It can't be just one more thing on my to-do list," she says. If you're worried she'll think you're quick on the trigger, tell her it's just a preview.

> Number of men who've received oral sex from a passenger: **2 in 3**

YOU HAVE 30 MINUTES

YOUR STRATEGY: PASS THE BATON. "Spend extra time focusing on each other's body and your intercourse will be more action-packed," says sexologist Carol Queen, PhD, author of *Exhibitionism for the Shy.* You're working toward a climax. She suggests kisses and gentle strokes in the sensitive nooks where the body bends, such as the wrists, the crooks of the elbows, and the backs of the knees. Nerves can predict where you're headed if you move in a straight line, so use a zigzag stroke instead.

YOU HAVE 1 HOUR

YOUR STRATEGY: WARM UP LONGER. Awaken your partner's eroge-nous zones all over her body by giving her a 20-minute massage. You'll both get a happy ending. "This isn't a health club," Dr. Queen says. "Keep her focused on the erotic nature of the massage, not the relax-ing, sleep-inducing side of it." Start with her back, then ask her to roll over so you can work your way toward her breasts and clitoris. And whatever you do, don't go all shiatsu on her breasts. A gentle, firm touch will suffice.

YOU HAVE ALL NIGHT

YOUR STRATEGY: TURN TRICKS. There are two ways to last all night. In tantric sex, you separate your orgasm from ejaculation. "Around 80 percent of men can do this after 3 months of training," says psychologist and sexologist Barnaby Barratt, PhD, author of *Sexual Health and Erotic Freedom*. Too New Age? Separate ejaculation from bedtime. The average postorgasm limp period in 30-year-olds is about half an hour. While you're waiting, try some new tricks. "It's all about variety," says Amy, 22. "Too much of one thing gets boring, even if that one thing is very good."

Start the Slow Burn

YOU MIGHT BE MICROWAVABLE—2 minutes on high and you're already peeling back the wrapper—but she's a slow cooker who requires a long simmer before you heat her to a rolling boil. It all starts with pressing the right buttons.

TALK IT UP. Start with your tongue. "Women want mental stimulation," says Ian Kerner, PhD, a certified sex therapist and author of

He Said/She Said

What's your favorite position for sex?

He Said		She Said
21%	Missionary	36%
40%	Doggy style	26%
33%	Cowgirl	30%
4%	Spooning	6%

Quantum physics, polyester, and the missionary position all separate humans from the rest of the animal kingdom. Alas, only the missionary position is bed-friendly. Women may love the increased intimacy, but the ol' vanilla shake is one of the hardest routes to female orgasm, says Ian Kerner, PhD, a sex therapist and the author of *She Comes First*. So change it up: "Don't thrust away like a porn star," says Dr. Kerner. "Instead, push your pelvic bone against her clitoris. Stay deep, using small movements of your pelvis to provide clitoral stimulation, which is usually abandoned in the missionary position." Satisfy her the standard way and she'll be more likely to try something different.

She Comes First: The Thinking Man's Guide to Pleasuring a Woman.
Ask her about her fantasies and talk about her turn-ons. "I told my
boyfriend about my fantasy of having sex in a fire station," says Jenny,
31. "Now, whenever we pass a firehouse, it's like our private signal
that we're both thinking about sex."

LOSE FOCUS. You have a one-track mind; she has a 24-track record-
ing studio. Get as much of her body in the game as you can before you
head south, says Dr. Kerner. Aim for her lips, behind her ears, the
nape of her neck, and the sides of her torso, just below her breasts.

GO AWAY. When you're apart from a romantic partner, hormones
are released that cause you to feel more attached and aroused when
you see that person again, says Bonnie Eaker Weil, PhD, author of
Make Up, Don't Break Up.

CHANGE THE PLAY. The *Men's Health* Girl Next Door, Nicole
Beland, suspects that many men take their lovemaking cues from
porn, but on fast-forward: "Two seconds of kissing, 4 seconds of breast
stimulation, 20 seconds of manual stimulation, 2 minutes of oral sex
for her, 20 minutes of oral sex for him, then intercourse for as long
and hard as they can keep it up." The more you vary the script, the
better she'll respond.

Go with the Flow

SEX ISN'T ALWAYS AS SMOOTH as late-night Cinemax would have you believe. "Even for the best of us, it can be awkward and messy," says Patti Britton, PhD, author of *The Art of Sex Coaching*. Here's some advice for handling five mood-breaking moments.

THE SITUATION: YOUR CLOTHES. WON'T. COME. OFF. Lighten up. "You don't stop being sexy just because your shoes are stuck. It's just entertainment," says Savanna Samson, Vivid Girl and star of the movie *The New Devil in Miss Jones*. If it bothers you, plan ahead with an easy-to-unclasp belt, a pullover shirt, and loafers. But remember: Women don't want to see a guy act like a stripper anyway.

THE SITUATION: THE NEIGHBORS ARE NOSY. Moan-proof your room. "If being vocal is part of her pleasure pattern, then you don't want to interrupt that," says Lou Paget, author of *365 Days of Sensational Sex*. Thicker drapes, cloth wall hangings, and towels tucked under doors can keep her cries from creeping through the cracks. (Or just play music.)

In the Bedroom

55 percent of men would like their lover to say "I want you—now" more often.

29 percent want her to talk dirty when she says it.

3 percent of men want to cut back on the foreplay.

20 percent think that the time foreplay takes would be better spent in sexy role-playing.

6 percent think that time would be better spent sleeping.

THE SITUATION: SHE'S NOT READY. YOU ARE. Lube up. "It doesn't mean she's not turned on," says Samson. It can be caused by any number of things—medication, dehydration, lack of foreplay.

THE SITUATION: SHE'S FAKING. YOU'RE NOT FOOLED. Call her bluff. "If this is someone you care about, don't let her get away with it," says Logan Levkoff, a New York–based sex educator. "Say, 'I have a feeling you're not enjoying this as much as you could be. Tell me what I can do to make it better.'" By finding out what she wants, you'll help her get there. If she still doesn't offer any advice, then let it go. You tried.

THE SITUATION: YOU NEED A CONDOM. Keep them handy but hidden. Condoms strung throughout your room like Christmas lights might be easy to access, but they're a turnoff. The nightstand is the obvious choice, says Levkoff. Bottom line: Make sure you can reach them without leaving the bed. And even if you have a 64-case from Sam's Club, keep them in user-ready batches of two or three.

ASK THE GIRL NEXT DOOR

The honest truth about women from our lovely neighbor

Is there a hookup timeline women secretly adhere to when they start dating a man?

Yes, but it varies, depending on how liberated a girl is and how horny she happens to feel on any given night. In general, if we're interested in pursuing a relationship with a man, the majority of my friends and I almost always avoid sex on the first two dates. (Oral sex included. Even if we're dying to—and would love to have the favor returned—we'll hold back for the sake of not feeling, or appearing, too easy.)

Why? We feel pressure—from society, from Mom, from all the times we've heard the word "slut"—to put a guy through a brief but vigorous evaluation before granting him access to our lacy underthings. Somehow, after the third round of dinner, drinks, and conversation, it feels okay if body parts start slipping into each other. For the record, I'm not saying you should ever expect sex (or even a tongue bath) on date three. I'm just saying you shouldn't be shocked if that's when the action begins.

She didn't have an orgasm the first time we had sex. How can I redeem myself?

Very few women expect the first time with a new guy to be explosively soul melding. Often, we're so self-conscious about having a new pair of eyes and hands on our bodies, we wouldn't climax even if you were Antonio Banderas licking the letter Z ad infinitum on our sweet spot. So don't worry about it. And don't sweat an abrupt ending, either. Initially, we'll take it as a compliment.

I've been having pretty conservative sex with a new girl I'm dating. How can I tell if she'll ever loosen up?

Take a peek in her bedside drawer. That's where most sexually open women keep their vibrator(s) and other fun stuff. One glance should give you an idea of what she's into. If there's nothing in there but a box of tissues, that doesn't necessarily mean she's squeaky clean. Why not try letting loose a little dirty talk next time you two are naked? Tell her a certain feline part of her body is beautiful and see if she responds positively or gets embarrassed. You could also point out a few sexy movies as you browse the video-rental aisles (some naughty faves: *Secretary*, *The Dreamers*, *Y Tu Mamá También*). Any woman who loves *Secretary* is bound to be up for fun.

What do women want for Valentine's Day? Give me a game plan, please.

If it's your first V Day together and you're in love: 1. Send her flowers at work—something other than clichéd roses. Try calla lilies or birds-of-paradise. 2. Give her a copy of your favorite novel, movie, or book of art or photography, or a mix CD of your favorites along with a recent book, DVD, or CD that—from what she's told you—she might like. 3. Give them to her (wrapped) during the dessert of a romantic dinner that you've whipped up at your place.

If she's a casual girlfriend and you want to keep it that way: Invite her out for a Valentine's Day dinner, but nix the gift.

If you've been dating for more than a year: Buy her something that could conceivably last forever: a painting by a well-respected local artist, a vintage watch or clock, pearl earrings (with small pearls that dangle below the ear), or a cuff bracelet with an embedded stone—jade or ruby.

What's Your Sexual IQ?

FORGET MENSA: The newest way to flaunt your intellectual superiority is through sexual IQ. "Sexual intelligence makes people more enlightened and aware," says Eve Marx, a sex expert and author of *What's Your Sexual IQ?* "A person who's sexually knowledgeable has something to contribute in almost any conversation on almost any topic, including politics, history, music, film, and art." Also? The more knowledge you gain, the better lovin' you'll make. Take this quiz to find out if you need to hit the books, the bedroom—or both.

1. **Cardamom, black pepper, cloves, and cinnamon are considered in India to be . . .**
   a. Libido killers
   b. Sleep inducing
   c. Contraceptives
   d. Aphrodisiacs

2. **Lubricants with petroleum oil as a base should never be used on what part of the body?**
   a. The vagina
   b. The mouth
   c. The breasts
   d. Any epidermis

3. Which of these fruits can a man eat to make his semen taste better?

a. Peaches

b. Watermelon

c. Passion fruit

d. Pomegranates

4. What birth control device is not advised if a woman has multiple partners?

a. A transdermal patch

b. A cervical cap

c. An IUD

d. A condom

5. The butterfly flick is . . .

a. A category of porn films

b. A form of sadomasochism

c. A type of fellatio

d. A form of lesbian oral sex

6. The "X" sexual position can be best described as:

a. The bottom person splays his or her arms and legs

b. The top person splays his or her arms and legs

c. The woman faces a wall with the man behind her

d. The woman sits astride the man, then both lie back

ANSWERS

1. (d) In Indian culture, cardamom, black pepper, cloves, and cinnamon are considered aphrodisiacs. Blended into a spicy drink with sugar and hot milk, they also happen to be chai tea.

2. (a) "Petroleum oil–based lubricants should never be used in or around the vagina because they're nearly impossible to wash out and

provide an ideal host environment to bacteria and viruses," Marx says. They also mean death to latex condoms.

3. (b) "Watermelon, like asparagus, is a natural diuretic and has the inspired effect [unlike asparagus] of making semen taste sweeter, almost ambrosial," Marx says.

4. (c) IUDs are not for women who have more than one partner because the string, necessary for removal, can trap bacteria and transmit disease, according to Marx.

5. (c) It's an oral sex technique that will drive you wild: She flicks her tongue lightly along the ridge on the underside of your penis, Marx says.

6. (d) Not for the inflexible, the "X," done with her on top and both of you lying back while clasping hands and wriggling, can prolong and intensify orgasm.

SCORE: GIVE YOURSELF 1 POINT FOR EACH CORRECT ANSWER

0–2 LIBIDIOT: There's more to life than the missionary position. Start tonight by trying a position new to you both.

3–4 MIDDLESEXER: You know more than enough to get by but not too much to be obsessive. Being caught in the middle isn't so bad.

5+ SEXPERIENCED: Try to be a little humble as you bask in your spectacular grasp of this wide and very tricky subject. If we think of any downsides to being so savvy, we'll let you know.

If you need a refresher course, *What's Your Sexual IQ?* is at Amazon.com or, for more serious study, enroll at the Erotic University of California (www.eroticuniversity.com).

5

GET
BETTER

We hope you don't encounter any problems in your sex life. But odds are you will sometime. This section covers the issues that can arise—including romatic ruts, ho-hum sex, erectile dysfunction, prostate cancer, and major marital crises—and offers solutions. We'll be delighted if you can skip right over this section because your sex life is humming along like a well-oiled machine. But if not, we're here for you. And we hope it all gets better, soon.

18 Ways to Feel Better in 5 Minutes

1. Sit in silence and count backward from 300. That's a 5-minute chunk of life gone to the gods, buddy. Do you miss it? Good. Now you see that killing time is a subtle form of suicide.

2. Hey, see that car wash? Pull in. A shower and shave for your ride polishes the brass on your balls.

3. Grab your girl and do whatever playful thing it is you do to brighten her day. A quick tango. A well-timed foot rub. A little flailing in the foyer. Attack now!

4. Unless you're lunching with the boss, no workday meal needs to last more than 5 minutes. Trail mix, tuna sandwich, some fresh fruit at your desk. Now you've saved time to exercise and get home at a reasonable hour.

5. Coffee-Free Break #1: Put your favorite song on headphones. Loud. Some "Sympathy for the Devil," perhaps? Feel better? Good, now get back to work.

6. Tell the younglings an anytime, anyplace story. Start with "Once upon a time, a man rode a horse into a forest." Make the rest up as you go. Marvel at how quickly they shut up.

7. Shred some old bank statements. Feels good, right? Very Enron-after-dark.

8. Go to an online bank site like Ingdirect.com and open

a savings account that will automatically deduct 5 percent of your net pay from your checking account every payday. Now, here's the important part: Forget the account exists.

9. Return that one call you don't want to return. Cut it off after 5 minutes; you now officially have better things to do.

10. Put up a new light fixture. You'll transform the room's dynamic. And it impresses women because any man who can perform basic electrical work is a man without fear.

11. You owe somebody, somewhere, a thank-you note.

12. Stretch your hamstrings. Makes every muscle feel better, doesn't it?

13. Self-abuse never hurts.

14. Coffee-Free Break #2: Three sets of 20 pushups. You don't even have to loosen your tie.

15. Great game when you're stuck in traffic: "What's That Guy Got That I Haven't?" Whatever it is, note your attitude toward that item or trait. You now have a good idea of what's motivating you these days.

16. Coffee-Free Break #3: Keep a funny book on hand. Some George Carlin, some David Sedaris, some old Calvin and Hobbes. Make five pages your 3 p.m. ritual.

17. She won't mind when the alarm clock goes off 5 minutes early tomorrow morning if she goes off soon after it.

18. While you're in line at the store, zone out on what's bothering you most about your life. Give yourself from now until the checkout cutie scans your first item to decide how you will solve this problem. See, you already know what the hell needs to be done. You're just not doing it yet.

Get Out of a Rut

We asked women for their advice on how to instantly upgrade your favorite positions and kick 'em up a notch

BY CELESTE PERRON

IT'S SO EASY to get lazy in bed. When the mood strikes, why contort like a Cirque du Soleil acrobat when 1) the fact that you're already having satisfying sex is more than most people accomplish and 2) a simple you're-on-top-tonight position can get the job done fine? But like anything easy—an energy bar for lunch, the treadmill at the gym—before long, you feel like you're missing out on the really fun stuff. So every once in a while (seriously, even just once a month), live it up a little. For the best way to do that naked, we asked experts and real women to share their proven strategies for getting new thrills out of those same old positions you know and love.

MISSIONARY

HER GRIPE #1: "I can't move the way I need to for an orgasm."

UPGRADE: To give her more wiggle room—for hip-grinding or to reach her clitoris with her fingers—sit back on your heels on the bed. Then have her lie back against a couple of pillows, place her legs on either side of your thighs, and grasp her hips and pull her pelvis toward your crotch. She can rest the bottoms of her feet on the bed for balance and leverage or wrap them around your waist. Stack pillows up high behind her to prevent all the blood from rushing to her head. Then again, that might just add to the excitement.

HER GRIPE #2: "I can't breathe when he's on top."

UPGRADE: It's impossible for her to get swept away by passion when she's oxygen-deprived. To give her more breathing space, support your weight on your forearms, suggests David Taylor, MD, who teaches a sexuality class for couples at Arizona's Miraval Life in Balance Resort. Have her put her hands on your chest to keep you there. Because your body is now at a different angle to hers, your penis will move down more toward her tailbone, so the shaft can rub against her clitoris when you thrust.

WOMAN ON TOP

HER GRIPE #1: "I don't get the G-spot stimulation I crave."

UPGRADE: Being on top is the best way for her to control the rhythm and level of penetration, and it's ideal for clitoral contact. But if she's looking for the almighty G-spot power-gasm, it's not going to do much for her. That's because her G-spot is located a few inches up the front wall of the vagina, Dr. Taylor says. Meaning just out of thrusting range if she's leaning forward or sitting upright, which most women tend to do. Instead she should lean back, placing her hands behind her on your quads if she needs the support. "From that angle his penis hits me in just the right place," says Amy K., 27, a lab technician from Maplewood, New Jersey.

HER GRIPE #2: "When I start to move, everything jiggles and I don't feel sexy enough to enjoy myself."

UPGRADE: Forget everything you've heard about how empowering and intimate it is to have sex with the lights on and just shut the damn things off—even the night-light. "If the reality is that [she feels] too self-conscious about [her] body to really let go in bed, then having sex in the dark will allow [her] to forget all about what [she looks] like and just have some fun," says Ian Kerner, PhD, a certified sex therapist and the author of *She Comes First: The Thinking Man's Guide to Pleasuring a Woman.* "There's no point in doing the empowering thing if it's not making [her] happy." When she's ready, fire up a candle and see how that makes her feel. Then light two, then three... until she feels comfortable doing it in broad daylight. On the beach!

HANDS AND KNEES

HER GRIPE #1: "It's a turn-on, but it doesn't give me the clitoral contact I need and want."

UPGRADE: No amount of wrangling the classic from-behind positions is going to move her clitoris to a different anatomical location. But she can free it up—along with her hands—if you kneel and rest your butt on your heels and then she lowers herself onto your lap, like she's sitting on a chair. Have her place her feet flat on the floor for balance and support—and so she can move up and down. If it sounds kind of like a workout, well, it is. But it feels so good she won't even notice that she's toning her calves and thighs.

HER GRIPE #2: "It feels really impersonal because I can't see his face or touch his body."

UPGRADE: The thing about having sex with you behind her is that it exposes the back of her body to a host of erotic sensations usually only played out in front. Plus, it taps into a naughty feeling that can be insanely hot. To get all of that without sacrificing any intimacy, try having her lie on her stomach while you lie flat on top of her (with some of your weight on your arms so you don't squash her). "It's more intimate because it provides lots of skin-on-skin contact," Dr. Taylor says. Even if she can't see you, she can hear your breath in her ear and feel the warmth of your body.

SIDE BY SIDE

HER GRIPE #1: "We have sideways sex when we're both too tired to move. It's not very erotic."

UPGRADE: Sleepy sex is so underrated, especially first thing in the a.m. Make the relaxed side-by-side position more exciting but just as effortless with what Julie D., 33, a personal trainer from Lakeville, New York, calls the "sideways split." Have her lie on her back while you lie on your side perpendicular to her so that your bodies form a T shape, where her torso is the stem of the T. Drape one of her legs over your shoulder and the other over your calf. "I can control how much stimulation I'm getting by spreading my legs farther (for more) or closing them a bit (for less)," Julie says.

HER GRIPE #2: "It's hard to figure out what to do with all our limbs."

UPGRADE: Damn those pesky arms and legs. To get them out of the way, try spooning, suggests Patti Britton, PhD, clinical sexologist and author of *The Art of Sex Coaching: Expanding Your Practice.* You both lie on your side, but her back is to you so you enter her from behind. Since she's facing away from you, your limbs don't get so tangled up. "This variation makes it easier for you to touch [her] breasts and clitoris, and it's still very intimate," Dr. Britton says.

STANDING UP

HER GRIPE #1: "We're about the same height, so standing-up sex works if I stand on my tiptoes, but then my calves get tired!"

UPGRADE: Her orgasms are elusive enough without having to maneuver around on her tippy-toes. To double the surface area she stands on and still get the extra few inches she needs for the perfect pelvic matchup, break out the highest heels she owns—platform boots, wedges, pumps, doesn't matter. If she doesn't have any heels that high, buy a cheap (but stable) pair for this purpose alone. She never has to wear them out of the house, and you'll get an extra thrill from seeing her in a pair of stilettos—which, for some still-a-mystery-to-women reason, guys seem to find hot.

HER GRIPE #2: "I'm shorter than he is, so he needs to lift me. But then his arms get tired and I feel like he's going to drop me."

UPGRADE: Lisa G., 31, a copywriter from Houston, solves that

Tweak It with a Toy

Two handy little accessories that heat up any position

Vibrating ring: Puts a motor on your mojo, giving you both a happy buzz (Petal Ring, $22, www.babeland.com).

Fingertip vibrator: Adds zip to any digit (Fukuoku 9000, $28, www.babeland.com).

problem by perching her butt on the edge of the desk in her home office (a sturdy table or kitchen counter will also work). "It has the spontaneous quality of standing-up sex, without him having to lift me," she says. To make the most of the countertop approach, have her stick to the very edge of it so her clitoris stays front and center for maximum contact with your penis.

Get Ready to Rumble

Perfect harmony? Save it for the barbershop quartet—smart couples get into conflict

IS ARGUING THE SOUND of a marriage chipping apart? Not necessarily. New research indicates that regular confrontation may well be the healthy pulse of a good relationship. In short, when it comes to opinions, a matching set may be out of style.

Not only are those couples who never argue a mystery to the rest of us nitpickers, but when it comes to happily-ever-after, they're missing the best part. Instead of turning their "fairy tale" into heartfelt reality with a few tie-me-up-tie-me-down disagreements, these partners avoid discussion altogether. Isolation rules instead of understanding and acceptance, then lack of intimacy kills the relationship. Lovely. And money, chores, sexual concerns, and kids are sources of tension for everyone, says Howard J. Markman, PhD, coauthor of *12 Hours to a Great Marriage: A Step-by-Step Guide for Making Love Last.*

Before you climb into the ring, though, know that "not every argument is a good one. Learn to differentiate the constructive from the destructive," Dr. Markman says. The danger signs, he adds, are feeling your anger escalate, saying no to her every suggestion, and thinking the worst of her. It's easy to rant about the idiocy of driving 3,000 miles with the "Check Oil" light on, but good arguing takes some skill and learning. Our experts explain how it's done.

START A TWO-MEMBER FIGHT CLUB. Pick a time and a place for "fight dates"—for example, before the gym (residual tension equals a vigorous workout). Don't go beyond the allocated time (Dr. Markman suggests 30 minutes) and avoid locations you want to associate with something enjoyable. No need to taint the dog run with memories of an especially heated discussion.

KNOW YOU MIGHT NOT REACH A RESOLUTION. Respect her right to a difference of opinion. And then don't brood about it. Brooders can develop unhealthy feelings of isolation.

PRACTICE ANGER MANAGEMENT. "Don't let the argument control you," Dr. Markman advises. If you can't stop fighting, you're not holding the reins.

KEEP TALKING. Giving her the silent treatment will make her feel lonely and look for intimacy somewhere else.

GO TO BED ANGRY. University of Washington relationship researcher John Gottman, PhD, found that a heightened emotional state makes communication and comprehension difficult. If the discussion is escalating but still going nowhere, ignore the conventional hoo-ha: Get into bed and sleep on it.

BE NICE WHEN YOU'RE NASTY. Putdowns, stonewalling, and yes-but's can spell trouble for a marriage if they're used more frequently than positive reinforcement. As angry as you are, choke out the words "I love you" at least once during the argument. Besides, you know you do, and it'll put you miles ahead of the game later on.

REMEMBER THAT LOVE MEANS SAYING MORE THAN "SORRY." Aaron Lazare, MD, a psychiatry professor at the University of Massachusetts Medical School, says that a simple "sorry" isn't good enough; explanation is key. Any argument, whether good or bad, should finish with a sincere apology. Flesh out "I don't know what came over me" into an honest conversation about what caused the problem. Then lock lips and make up.

So there.

Save Your Penis

Here's how to spot a problem before things get, ahem, out of hand

BY GARY STEIN

IT BEGAN AS A SMALL SLIT, like a paper cut. The skin was unusually dry and irritated most of the time. I tried moisturizers, Vaseline, even Blistex during one office emergency. Nothing helped. It would tease me by clearing up temporarily and making unannounced return engagements. Actually, I became attuned to its comings and goings. After all, a cut at the base of your penis gets your attention. It's uncomfortable and inconvenient, and insists on very gentle handling. Even that all-important final shake during a visit to the bathroom was enough to make it tear. I decided—after much procrastination—to take it to the professionals.

I went to my general practitioner, a real guy's guy. Naturally, he yanked on a pair of latex gloves and gave me that look a doctor gives when he needs you to do something awkward. I activated my anti-embarrassment shield, lowered my pants, and showed him the equipment.

What are the odds of having a cut on the only part of your body that changes size? Any genius knows that stretching and shrinking don't promote healing. And not only is such a cut uncomfortable during sex, it also makes it impossible to stay focused, which leads to no sex at all. I think I blurted all that out during the exam.

Afterward, he agreed with my layman's diagnosis: It was dry skin. He gave me samples of ointments and told me to call him in 2 weeks if the situation hadn't improved, and then we'd think about the next step—seeing a dermatologist.

"But I don't think we're headed down that road," he said with a confident smile.

Two weeks later, at the dermatologist's office, I was given another thorough exam by a doctor wearing latex gloves. He, too, agreed that the skin was dry. However, the dermatologist, Dr. Connelly, had far more effective ointments. And if it didn't heal in 2 weeks, he would take a small biopsy "just to be sure." Then at least we'd have a handle on this whole thing and find "just the right ointment." That was just peachy. The word "biopsy" was scary enough, but hey, we weren't there yet. No reason to jump the gun.

Skin Care, Down There

Even if you never develop skin cancer on your most valuable skin, there are other flesh maladies in that area that can cause panic attacks. Not to worry, says Adnan Nasir, MD, PhD, a professor of dermatology at the University of North Carolina at Chapel Hill. You simply need to identify what you might be dealing with.

Sudden red, itchy rash. Contact dermatitis (doctor-speak for an allergic reaction). You could be allergic to the latex in your condoms, the detergent in your tighty whities, or even the lotion or perfume your girlfriend uses. One way to know for sure is to have your doctor do an allergy test. In the meantime, try a hypoallergenic detergent or a polyurethane condom, and pop an antihistamine like Benadryl or Claritin to relieve the itch.

Bright red, itchy rash where your legs meet your groin. Jock itch. First, switch to boxers. (Sorry, boxer briefs are not a compromise.) Then slap on a little Gold Bond powder in the morning to keep your undercarriage dry as you sweat through the day. In more severe cases, your doctor might prescribe an antifungal cream.

Patches of yellow, greasy flakes with pinpoint bleeding when scratched. Psoriasis. You might find similar patches on your elbows,

Two additional weeks later, I was waiting for my penis biopsy. When my name was called, I was suddenly aware of all the people sitting around me in Dr. Connelly's waiting room. I walked toward the open door with a bounce in my step. No way was I going to walk like a man who had a problem with his penis.

Dr. Connelly assured me it was going to be quick and painless. He'd have to inject an anesthetic at the base of the penis, but he'd be using a very tiny needle. I'm not sure why he thought that a tiny

knees, belly button, or scalp, and your finger- and toenails may begin to look bumpy. Swimming in saltwater might clear this up. You can also use a hydrocortisone cream or a tar shampoo like Neutrogena T/Gel. Tough cases earn a prescription for a topical steroid or a nonsteroidal anti-inflammatory cream.

Redness with yellow, greasy scales, but no bleeding. Seborrheic dermatitis. This can also cover your sternum, and you may develop it near your eyebrows and behind your ears. Treat it with a selenium sulfide shampoo, such as Selsun Blue, or one containing salicylic acid or ketoconazole.

Rash with white, powdery scales in the folds of the skin. Eczema. It can also show up in the crooks of your elbows and on the backs of your knees. Treat it with Sarna or Aveeno anti-itch lotion or a hydrocortisone cream. Prescription remedies include Protopic and Zonalon.

Any one of the above that doesn't go away after treatment, plus irregular bumps. Possible skin cancer. You'll need to visit a specialist for a biopsy of the affected area.

needle would make it more inviting. I also didn't need to see a tiny needle penetrating my wang, so I didn't look.

After the anesthetic kicked in, I felt nothing as Dr. Connelly worked. Ah, but my imagination was right there to supply all the emotional discomfort: A man was scraping flesh from my penis. Fortunately, it didn't take long. Dr. Connelly said it didn't look like anything serious at all, but we'd have to rule things out. "Hey, at least we'll know exactly what to call it," he said.

The following week, Linda, Dr. Connelly's nurse, phoned me, and damn if they hadn't found something to call it: "Superficial skin cancer," she said.

Two weeks later, I was back in the waiting room. I was in line for a Mohs procedure, in which the doctor fillets a layer of skin at a time and looks for cancerous cells at the perimeter of the offending area. If he finds some, he does it again. And again—as often as he has to, until there's nothing left to fillet. They examine the tissue under a microscope while you sit and read magazines.

Superficial skin cancer. Sheesh. I simply could not imagine the C word being associated with any body part of mine, let alone that one. I wasn't too hot about the word "superficial," either. If it's superficial, then it's not worth having. It shouldn't even have the right to be called cancer and scare everyone (me) like that. And I didn't want the word "superficial" used anywhere near my penis. There's nothing superficial about it, thank you.

Finally, Linda called me in. She really did try her best to make the situation comfortable. She told me that during the operation I would have this nice, big, double-folded sheet over my lap. I'd be completely covered, except for the giant hole cut in the middle. Yeah, that's where the very thing I'm most embarrassed about showing off would protrude like a gopher poking its head out to see if all's clear.

It got even better when Dr. Connelly said he'd need Linda to assist. My heart sank. So did something else. Everyone knows a smart penis shrinks when it's scared. I had a damn thimble on my hands. I wanted to shout all kinds of disclaimers: "You should see this thing in action! You could hurt yourself!"

But if there's one lesson I learned throughout this whole ordeal—beyond the devastating link between pride and penis—it's that it's impossible to maintain any significant level of embarrassment for a long period of time. You simply succumb. Soon I even stopped assuming they felt sorry for my wife.

I had to go in three times that day before he was finished. By the time I took my last long walk, I was actually looking forward to a third injection of anesthesia. I was getting healthy, after all. And the shots were making my penis extremely swollen. I found a reason to strut a little bit. My pride was returning. You know, we really are very resilient animals.

I'm happy to report that, a year later, I remain free of anything superficial.

QUICKIES

Check the Plumbing

AS MEN AGE, we need to consider the heart/erection connection. "All health issues have effects on your penis," says Steven Lamm, MD, the author of *The Hardness Factor: How to Achieve Your Best Health and Sexual Fitness at Any Age.* "A 50-year-old man who is healthy is probably performing as well sexually as an out-of-shape 30-year-old who smokes and drinks." Dr. Lamm recommends these lifestyle changes to keep your member in good standing after the teenage years.

ELIMINATE THE FAT AROUND YOUR GUT. Abdominal fat blocks the testosterone that should be available to you, which in turn affects sexual functioning. A fat gut is a bad marker for overall health—including your sexual health, says Dr. Lamm.

DO A CARDIO WORKOUT DAILY. When you exercise, bloodflow increases; blood rushes through the endothelial cells (the lining of the blood vessels) and stimulates them to make more nitric oxide, a key chemical involved in producing erections. "The healthier a man is, the more nitric oxide he produces, and the harder his erection is," says Dr. Lamm.

GIVE UP BUTTS. "Absolutely do not smoke—that just clenches down on your blood vessels and prevents them from being reactive," he says. Smoking restricts penile bloodflow and weakens erections, making smokers twice as likely to experience erectile dysfunction.

AVOID BIG MEALS AND ALCOHOL BEFORE SEXUAL ENCOUNTERS. Give yourself 2 hours between dinner and sex. Would you eat a big meal before playing a full-court basketball game? "If all your blood is going to your gut, it's not going to go to your pelvic area," Dr. Lamm says.

Don't Think Small

Obsessing over penis size can turn you into a lousy lover. Men who think they have small penises may think they can't satisfy their partners. This can make it difficult to maintain an erection, in what is known as psychogenic erectile dysfunction, says Rany Shamloul, MD, a researcher at the University of Saskatchewan, in Canada. The irony: His new research on men who complained of having small penises showed most were not as small as they thought. Here are more of his findings, published in the journal *Adult Urology*.

94 percent of men overestimated normal flaccid penis size.

Average guess as to flaccid penis size: **5.1 inches**

Actual normal length of a flaccid penis: **3 to 4 inches**

Normal length of a stretched penis: **4.7 to 5.1 inches** (It's roughly the same as erect-penis length but is considered a more accurate way to measure.)

45 percent had a stretched-penis length of 5.1 inches or greater.

0 percent had an "abnormal" measurement (less than 2.75 inches).

59 percent traced their short-penis complexes to childhood, when they began comparing their penises to those of friends.

41 percent said their problems started in adolescence, when they began viewing erotic films and magazines.

86 percent said their size worries vanished after they were educated about average penis size and informed of their own measurements.

TAKE SUPPLEMENTAL INSURANCE. Pop two omega-3 fatty-acid supplements daily totaling at least 300 milligrams of docosahexaenoic acid (DHA) and 400 mg of eicosapentaenoic acid (EPA) as a kind of insurance on your heart and penis health. And consider taking the antioxidants pycnogenol (80 milligrams) and L-arginine (3 grams) daily. They'll shield your endothelium from harm and facilitate the use of nitric oxide.

Consider This

FOR THE FIRST TIME, a public survey shows a correlation between erection problems and major illness.

A national poll of 4,000 men found that of those who reported difficulty getting and keeping an erection, 45 percent also had high blood pressure and 20 percent suffered from diabetes. "The penis truly is the thermometer of men's health," says Ridwan Shabsigh, MD, an associate professor of urology at Columbia University. The survey of men ages 40 to 60—conducted by Harris Interactive for *Best Life*, Columbia-Presbyterian Medical Center, and Cialis—is the first time a self-reported public poll has shown the correlation between erectile dysfunction (ED) and cardiovascular health.

Men typically wait 3 to 4 years after experiencing ED before seeking a doctor's help, according to Dr. Shabsigh. "Some men are literally dying of embarrassment, because ED often hints at a potentially life-threatening problem," he says.

OTHER SURVEY STATISTICS:

Men would prefer to dance in public or give a speech to a crowd than submit to a rectal exam.

Only 30 percent said they'd admit in public to ED for $10,000. But nearly 50 percent would admit to fantasizing about a neighbor for the same financial incentive.

Keep Your Prostate Healthy

THIS YEAR, 232,000 MEN will be diagnosed with prostate cancer. Don't let yourself be one of them. Here are four ways to keep your prostate healthy (and your erections hard).

EAT A TOMATO, OR FOUR. Men who ate two to four servings of raw tomatoes per week reduced their risk of prostate cancer by 26 percent, a study review in the *Journal of Nutrition* found. If you don't like tomatoes, go with pizza or marinara sauce.

PUT DOWN THE HAMBURGER. Fat lowers circulating levels of prostate-specific antigen (PSA), according to a recent study, meaning excess pounds could skew the results of your PSA test. It also makes digital rectal exams more difficult and therefore less accurate.

SEE THE LIGHT. Men who live in the sunniest states have a 32 percent lower prostate-cancer risk, one study found. Take a vitamin D supplement (aim for 1,000 IU per day) and save your skin.

CHECK YOUR FOLATE. High folate intake helps men halve their risk of prostate cancer, one study found. Aim for 400 micrograms per day, from supplements, cooked spinach (100 micrograms per cup), or fortified cereal.

Let Her Go

BREAKING UP ISN'T HARD—until she tries to persuade you to stay. Now what? Relationships are like movies—a bad ending ruins the whole thing. Maybe you think it's over (you've said as much), but she still harbors hope. Any mixed message fuels her pipe dream, explains Bonnie Eaker Weil, PhD, author of *Make Up, Don't Break Up*. Here are five tips for a clean getaway.

MAKE A BREAK. The dump must be direct. "Don't let your fear or conflict avoidance lead you to say something like 'Maybe we should take a break' when what you mean is 'This isn't going to work out for me,'" says David Wexler, PhD, author of *When Good Men Behave Badly: Change Your Behavior, Change Your Relationship.*

HELP HER LEAVE. It's possible she's idealizing you. "You must make her see the bad parts of you," Dr. Weil says. Remind her how lazy and self-centered you are, that you'll never change, and that she's better off without you. While still making it clear it's over, help her self-esteem by apologizing for things you may not necessarily think are your fault. "Say something like 'I can't believe how selfish I was. It's not your fault,'" says Dr. Weil. She'll stop thinking that if she changes, you'll come back.

FORGET "BEING FRIENDS." "While some couples can break up and remain friends, it's rare, and planting that idea during a breakup can lead her to expect more," says Les Parrott, PhD, author of *Love Talk*. Tell her you both need to move on, or that you'll need a couple of months to heal. That emotional divorce is crucial, says Dale Larson, PhD, a professor of counseling psychology at Santa Clara University.

SHED TEARS. Show your grief and she'll feel like less of a loser. If she sees that you're moving forward while she's crying through reruns of *Ally McBeal,* she may cling, Dr. Larson says.

DON'T RELAPSE. If your ex shows up at your door buck naked, hand her a robe. Helen Fisher, PhD, author of *Why We Love: The Nature and Chemistry of Romantic Love,* says ex sex can mean long-term regrets. "Think the kiss through to the finale," she says. (Not that finale.) "You'll be with someone you don't love and you'll feel incredibly trapped. It makes that kiss less enticing." If all else fails, run.

Science of Sex

What comes first, the mind or the body? Researchers asked nearly 800 men and women to describe their orgasms, choosing from 28 adjectives. Participants also rated physical intensity (spasms, throbbing) and emotional experiences (love, ecstasy, satisfaction). The results, published in the *Journal of Sex & Marital Therapy,* indicate that orgasmic pleasure may have more to do with mental factors, like relationship satisfaction, than with physical factors, such as the anatomical location of sensations. And not just for women. "Men's orgasm experiences may be more influenced by emotional factors—for example, emotional closeness with a partner—than previously thought," says study author Kenneth Mah, PhD.

Defuse Her Anger

SHE'S FURIOUS, you're flummoxed. So defuse her anger in a way she understands: by talking it to death. "The key is building toward a discussion. It doesn't matter if it's good, bad, or ugly," says Sergeant Scottie Frier, a crisis negotiator in the Lexington County Sheriff's Department in South Carolina. "If you're going to end up in a crisis again with that person, you need to have built that trust."

FIND HER FUSE: ESTABLISH A PERIMETER. Start by detecting bluffs. A crisis situation could be just a call for attention. "Women sometimes pick fights to gauge a man's level of interest and commitment," says Nancy Fagan, author of *The Complete Idiot's Guide to Romance.* "It might not have to do with what she's nagging about." And don't just blame monthly mood swings. "Under the anger are usually the primary feelings of hurt or frustration," says Maryland-based sex educator Charles Miron, PhD. "If you dive under the anger and deal with those buried emotions, you're more likely to get a mutually positive outcome." Your telltale sign: hostages. If she's holding back on sex, this could be serious. "If there are problems in the bedroom, it's because there's anger," says Susan Sheppard, a relationship coach and the author of *How to Get What You Want from Your Man Anytime.*

SET THE TONE: STOW THE BULLHORN. "You want to set the tone, the mood, the tempo, and the agenda of the discussion," says Robert Mayer, author of *How to Win Any Argument: Without Raising Your Voice, Losing Your Cool, or Coming to Blows.* Let her vent. If she wants to explode, throw on a bomb suit. "Nobody is going to listen to logic until the emotional part has been dealt with," says Mayer. Frier suggests saying, "I understand that you're upset, but it's hard for me to work through this if you keep screaming." That reality shock makes her assess her behavior. Use eye contact to show you're listening—rapt, even—and paraphrase her points to acknowledge that you're hearing what she's saying. But be careful of land mines: "In any cross-examination," says Ken Suggs, president of the Association of Trial Lawyers of America, "it's important that you know the answer you're going to get."

RESOLVE THE CRISIS: SEAL THE DEAL. "Now it becomes a cooperative effort," Frier says. Let's say your position is logical and you hold the moral high ground. "If you force something on her, you're going to end up with a bitter, resentful girlfriend," says Mayer. So cut a deal. "You want to make her feel like she's part of the process," Frier says. Ask her to offer solutions. If she makes a demand that's reasonable, work to try to gain something from it. Start small. "In a hostage situation, the first thing we do is ask

> Percentage of women who say that birth control pills make them moodier: **16**

them to release all the hostages, knowing they'll say no," says Frier. "Then we compromise by asking them to release one. I just won because I'm going to get a hostage out, and they think they've won because they only have to give up one guy." Her emotional hostages need some air, too.

ASK THE GIRL NEXT DOOR

The honest truth about women from our lovely neighbor

How should I respond to a woman if she asks me if I'm gay? (I'm not.)

It must be frustrating when a woman you're interested in thinks you'd make a great match with her hot cousin Tad, but there are two reasons why the gay question is not a dis: "The idea that gay men are less masculine or sexy than straight men? Gone. When my friends and I are sitting in hot tubs naming sin-worthy men, rock star Rufus Wainwright and hunky fashion designer Tom Ford come up long before Brad Pitt." It seems that every attractive man a single woman comes across turns out to be taken, gay, or on drugs. So if your belt matches your shoes, a girl gets nervous. Given that, I suggest you respond by flashing her an easygoing smile and saying, "How about I take you out for drinks Friday night and you can find out for yourself?"

I take Viagra because I need it. Do women want to know that information? If so, when do I spill it?

Viagra, when used properly, is a treatment for a health condition, not some seedy lie hiding in your pants. And the only health conditions you're obligated to reveal before you sleep with a woman are the ones she could catch. Otherwise, what medication you take is a topic for a long-term relationship. When things get serious, let her know.

Do most women think it's cheating when their significant other goes to a strip club?

Only about 1 in 12 women is cool with her man going to a strip club. The rest of us have reached this consensus: On the one hand, we can understand that watching naked women dance is a way for you to revel in the eroticism of the female body and bond with your friends in an old-school atmosphere. That may be tacky and a bit sexist, but it's not cheating. On the other hand, a man who gets a lap dance is—without question—having a sexual experience with another woman. It's not personal or meaningful, and no fluids are exchanged, but it's still sex. (We know about the part where Missy treats your face like a bicycle seat.) That is cheating. If you want to do right by your woman, look, but don't ever touch.

What goes through a woman's mind when she discovers her guy's porn stash?
As long as it's within the limits of what I consider normal—two or three magazines or DVDs of straightforward heterosexual or girl-on-girl stuff—I figure he uses porn in a healthy way: when he wants to up the intensity of a solo experience, or just get work or other stressors off his mind. If his stash is huge, or includes some truly twisted or violent themes, I consider it a likely sign that he has some suppressed guilt or shame about sex. Next stop: a joint appearance at the sex therapist's.

What's Your Sexual Age?

ERECTIONS FOLLOW A fairly predictable evolution: They get less hard with every decade and with declines in overall health. But you can improve the strength of yours and even turn back your sexual clock by getting fitter and healthier through diet and exercise, says Steven Lamm, MD, author of *The Hardness Factor: How to Achieve Your Best Health and Sexual Fitness at Any Age.* "There really is a correlation between the crispness and reactivity of blood vessels in the penis and overall physical health," he says. We asked Lamm to suggest a simple self-test to determine your penis's prowess.

1. **What's your blood pressure?**
   a. Top number below 120 and bottom number below 80
   b. Top number between 120 and 139 and bottom number between 80 and 89
   c. Top number between 140 and 159 and bottom number between 90 and 99
   d. Top number 160 or more and bottom number 100 or more

2. **What is your LDL (bad) cholesterol level?**
   a. Less than 100 mg/dL
   b. 100 to 129 mg/dL
   c. 130 to 159 mg/dL
   d. 160 to 189 mg/dL
   e. 190 mg/dL or higher

3. Do you smoke?

a. Yes

b. No

4. Rate the level of hardness of your erection.

a. Soft

b. Soft/hard

c. Hard

d. Very hard

e. Like a steel I beam

5. Where does your erection point?

a. Slightly downward, or less than 90 degrees from your thighs

b. Roughly parallel with the floor, or 90 degrees from your thighs

c. Slightly upward, or 100 to 120 degrees from your thighs

d. Angled more than 120 degrees upward from your thighs

6. You are able to achieve an erection . . .

a. Before you reach the fifth floor while riding an elevator with a hot woman

b. While close dancing with her

c. Even before you get her clothes off

d. Within a minute or two of stimulation

e. Only after 10 minutes of intense foreplay

f. Can't achieve an erection without pharmaceutical help

7. What is your refractory period? In other words, how long does it take you to achieve another erection after you've had an orgasm?

a. A day or more

b. More than 4 hours

c. 2 to 4 hours

d. 20 minutes to 2 hours

e. Can achieve multiple erections minutes apart

8. How many orgasms can you have in a day?

a. Only one

b. One good, one so-so

c. Two great ones

d. Three

e. Four

f. More than four

SCORING

Add up your points and compare with the chart at right:

1. a=0, b=1, c=2, d=3

2. a=0, b=1, c=2, d=3, e=4

3. a=2, b=0

4. a=5, b=4, c=3, d=2, e=1

5. a=4, b=2, c=2, d=0

6. a=0, b=1, c=2, d=3, e=4, f=10

7. a=4, b=3, c=2, d=1, e=0

8. a=5, b=4, c=3, d=2, e=1, f=0

Your Points	Your Sexual Age
26 OR MORE	85
24 OR 25	75
21 TO 23	65
17 TO 20	55
13 TO 16	45
9 TO 12	35
6 TO 8	30
4 OR 5	25
3	15

Note: This is not a diagnostic medical test. It is designed to make you aware of the impact health and age have on erectile function. If you're concerned about erectile function, visit your family doctor or a urologist. The inability to maintain an erection for sex can be a symptom of a serious medical condition, such as depression, high blood pressure, diabetes, or heart disease.

6

SURVIVE RELATION-SHIPS

We admit, "survive" is a little overly dramatic. But relationships aren't easy—or else half of all marriages wouldn't end in divorce and divorce lawyers would drive Hyundais instead of BMWs. In our effort to keep as much business away from those folks as we can, we offer our very best relationship advice. Here's how to enhance your relationship in 18 easy steps, 7 critical things to know before shacking up, our secrets to losing your fear of commitment, and the best ways to affair-proof your relationship by keeping the ho-hum humdrum out of your humble abode. We offer you our best for a lifetime of laughter, love, and great sex.

18 Ways to Enhance Yourself and Your Relationship

1. Resist Cinemax. Don't watch sex; experience it with that underserved woman in your bed. She's waiting for a suggestion. Make it.

2. Drink two fewer beers per week. That's 15,600 fewer calories in a year, and 5 pounds off by December.

3. Seduce her. Again. You'll be a happier person overall.

4. End a feud. Divert that energy into reviving poker night or some other buddy ritual. You need friends, too.

5. Play hooky on a few Wednesdays. Ignore voice messages and e-mail. Break rules like a 15-year-old whose parents are in Europe.

6. Build a bigger chest by March. Your simple plan: Watch the new season of 24 and do 10 pushups every time someone is tortured.

7. Suspend judgment of others on the highway. You make mistakes, too. Your last words shouldn't be "I'll show that bastard how to change lanes..."

8. Find a new way to pleasure her. Just starting the discussion can only lead to good things.

9. Set a goal. Tell no one. You're the only audience that matters. Master options trading? Hone your sand-trap exit strategies? Adopt a ladies-first approach to orgasm? You can do it, man!

10. Weigh yourself every morning. You'll be 29 percent less likely to gain 5 pounds. Really.

11. That moneymaking scheme of yours? Chat up five people who know the field, and five potential customers. Your next steps will be obvious.

12. Once a month, remind your boss you have balls. His authority goes only so far.

13. Learn all about fish—how to buy it, prep it, cook it. Because any man can dial takeout. But if you know fish, you'll eat smarter and live better and longer.

14. Stop staring at your hairline like an infant perplexed by a mobile.

15. Try four things you decided you hate. The ballet. Brussels sprouts. French lessons. Yoga. Why? Because two of them will work for you.

16. Make Mexican your default health food. Really, is there better eating than chicken, black beans, guacamole, and fresh salsa slopped on a plate?

17. Savor her. Catch her eye. Steal her heart. Feeling especially daring? Take her hand.

18. Start now. Positive changes, just like winning streaks, have a momentum all their own.

Shack Up

After the nonstop sex stops, use these tips for coexisting with a woman under the same roof

BY CHRIS CONNOLLY

IT DIDN'T TAKE LONG for me to realize that living with my girlfriend might require a slight adjustment period; we were still packing my stuff for the move to her place. I was lugging yet another heavy box through the kitchen on my way downstairs to the van, sweat streaming from my face, when Kirsten looked up from the cutting board she was carefully wrapping in newspaper.

"Oooh!" she sighed, spotting a snow globe we picked up during our first vacation together. "Remember where we bought this?"

I'm dying, she's dawdling. Maybe, just maybe, I started to think, Kirsten and I are not a single soul split betwixt two bodies.

Shacking up is a good way to save on rent and get lovin' without scheduling an appointment. But there's more to moving in than sex and money. "You're agreeing to share your lives, not just your living space," says Marshall Miller, proprietor of Unmarried.org and coauthor of *Unmarried to Each Other: The Essential Guide to Living Together as an Unmarried Couple.* "When a couple agree to move in together, they're often at a high point of feeling good about one another. But cohabitation quickly gets to the nitty-gritty of life."

Come to grips with these seven revelations before you move in together and maybe the relationship will outlast the lease.

YOUR RELATIONSHIP WILL CHANGE

Now that you're "domestic partners," things are going to be different around here, mister. Effective immediately. "Cohabitation," says Miller, "is a lot like turning the TV to your favorite channel—and then leaving it on 24-7. You're bound to see some stuff you don't like so much."

For one thing, your beloved won't always look as hot as she used to when you picked her up on a Saturday night. Yes, that gorgeous lady is still in there somewhere, but now you'll have to get acquainted with the stinky chick who just came home from the gym, and the testy woman who's too preoccupied with the Weiner account to succumb to your frisky antics. Know this and accept it before going in.

YOUR SEX LIFE WILL CHANGE BIG-TIME

Not every night will end with the two of you naked, sticky, and sweaty. "When you live apart, you make time for sex—any minute you can get your hands on each other, you do," says Logan Levkoff, PhD, a New York City–based sex educator. "But when you're around one another all the time, the frequency of sexual activity may taper off. The solution is still making time for intimacy but changing your expectations. Realize that you can be intimate without having intercourse."

This means you'll need to accept the transition from hardware to software: less bonking, more spooning.

GENTLEMEN, START YOUR SWIFFERS

Divvying up domestic chores is one of the first things a cohabiting couple needs to discuss. Forget equality. "Everything doesn't have to be fifty-fifty," says Andrew Cherlin, PhD, author of *The Deinstitutionalization of American Marriage* and *Public and Private Families: An Introduction.* "If one of you works 50 hours a week and the other 25, there's nothing wrong with the less busy person taking on more of the housework."

Reduce the tension and tedium by volunteering for housework that doesn't drive you crazy. My buddy Josh hates washing silverware, but unlike most people, he doesn't mind scrubbing pots and pans. So after dinner he tackles the heavy metal while his wife merrily tends to the flatware. Compromises like this make a relationship work.

LOVE IS ANNOYING

It's inevitable: Now that you're living together, you're gradually going to discover each other's irritating habits. She makes a weird noise while she sleeps; you fart with abandon.

"One way to soften the blow is to try living together for a spell before you actually move in," Dr. Levkoff advises. "Just make sure it's a normal, mundane week so you'll get a real feel for what the morning rush is like, what the dishwashing situation is like."

The key, no matter how long you've been living together: When confronted with one of those fingernails-on-the-chalkboard-of-life moments, don't let it slide. But resist the urge to bite her head off.

Am I Normal?

During fights with my girlfriend, I'll let awful insults slip out. That's typical, right?

No. Your brain's brake, the prefrontal cortex (PFC), isn't active enough. You're blurting before thinking. Could be too little sleep, too much alcohol, or a lack of empathy. Retrain your brain to be more thoughtful. After an insult slips out, ask your girlfriend how you made her feel and allow yourself to feel bad about the behavior. Guilt can help you become more empathetic. When tension builds, use my "bathroom technique": Grab a book and spend 10 minutes in the bathroom. If you're really upset, make it a big book.

Wynne Whitman, coauthor of *Shacking Up: The Smart Girl's Guide to Living in Sin Without Getting Burned*, prefers a gentler, more constructive approach. "Instead of yelling, 'Why the hell do you always leave your briefcase on the floor?' try saying, 'It makes me very happy when you put your briefcase away.' This phrasing makes your roomie think she's doing you a favor, and it doesn't seem like a chore."

YOU'RE NOT ENGAGED—YET

There is a subtext to this move. According to the *Annual Review of Sociology*, about 75 percent of cohabiting couples say they plan to marry their partner. Additionally, 55 percent of marriages today are preceded by cohabitation. But not every couple that lives together is destined to walk down the aisle together. "We interviewed a woman who assumed that moving in with her boyfriend was an engagement," Whitman recalls. "But she never actually spoke to her boyfriend about it. When she found out he didn't want to marry her, she was heartbroken."

Like it or not, when you move in with your girlfriend, you're sending a message: "I'm ready to settle down." Unless you've made it clear that living together is not a formal engagement, she's likely to think there's a diamond ring in her immediate future.

YOUR PROBLEMS ARE WEDLOCKED

Live-in couples have to deal with many of the same issues spouses do. One of the thorniest is keeping the relationship fresh. Because you're no longer dating, it's crucial that you maintain the relationship's fun factor. For starters, don't become too reliant on one another.

"It's really important not to put all your eggs in one basket," says Whitman. "Often, people make the mistake of giving up all their other relationships just because they're living with someone. You need to spend time apart to appreciate the time you spend together."

LIVE AND LEARN—TOGETHER

You may discover, as I did, that your girlfriend's good qualities more than make up for her uselessness as a mover. Or you may find that her insistence on replacing the toilet-paper roll so it feeds from the bottom is too much for you to take. Either way, you're in this together. Find a way to get over, through, or around every obstacle and your relationship may evolve into something even more wonderful than convenient sex.

"There's a misconception that people who cohabit never want to get married," says Whitman. "I disagree. I think, on the contrary, they want to make sure they have only one marriage. They want to make sure this is the right person before they commit."

And before they have to lug all those boxes back down 13 flights of stairs.

Lose Your Fear of Commitment

Here's our perfect formula for pain-free marriage. Now, if we can just get women to sign on . . .

BY TAD LOW

I'M 38 AND HAVE NEVER been married. And it's not happening until they change the rules. It's not like I haven't enjoyed satisfying companionship with long-term girlfriends or entertained fuzzy-focused fantasies of toasting cans of Ensure at my 50th wedding anniversary. It's just that my gut instinct tells me our marital system is woefully broken.

Well, gut instinct and these facts: The U.S. Census Bureau predicts that if you're married and under 45, there's about a 50 percent chance it won't last. What happens, statistics show, is that growing discontent leads to separation at the 7-year mark. You spend 9 months "trying to work things out," perhaps even enjoying the separation sex, but ultimately this fails. One of you, most likely she, files for divorce. A few months before your eighth anniversary (bronze, so no biggie), your marriage is erased from the public record.

Quickly, probably within 6 months, you meet someone else. This time, you promise yourself, you'll take things slowly. You flirt, court, and date seemingly forever, making sure she's The Real One, then dive into your second marriage 3 years and a few months after your divorce was final. Good luck. You'll need it. There's a one-in-five chance this one will fail, too.

And so it goes.

I know, I know: Your marriage is different. Except that it's not. There are no statistical anomalies here; it's not like those grass-isgreener Massachusettsians are bringing down the national average. No, across this great land of ours, marriages like yours are failing half the time. Look over at the guy in the next cube: Odds are, one of you is doomed.

Perhaps now you understand my position: I see people all around me readying themselves for a huge leap of faith, ignoring the fact that the person who packs the parachutes gets it right less than half the time.

That's me on the tarmac with neon flares, shouting, "Don't get on that plane!"

I work in TV. I invent programs and try to sell them to networks. If they like my pitch, we draw up a contract. If it works out, I get paid and the show hits the air. If not, we all walk away. No hurt feelings or lost friends. Everyone knows going in that it's a short-term experiment.

By contrast, think about all the misery engendered by your standard broken marriage: hurt, animosity, psychological damage to the kids, money down the drain, private investigators. It also leaves both partners saddled with the stigma of "failure" and keeps an army of divorce lawyers in BMWs.

But still we pretend marriage is permanent. The tented receptions, calligraphy-scripted invites, Vivaldi-playing string quartets… they're props on a set of make-believe. Your odds are better at a rigged carnival arcade, and yet we, as a culture, continue to throw dollars at the barker for more basketballs.

Most of my friends and family have stepped right up. My two brothers are married with kids, and my parents have been together for 40 years, so it's not that I haven't had a chance to view "successful" unions up close. What I see is a lot of compromise fading the color of each partner's distinctiveness, leaving behind a bland blob of comfort and routine. It's this loss of self that either gets subsumed as acceptance or explodes in defiance (aka divorce).

When a good friend of my parents recently walked out on his wife of 35 years, he was vilified as a rake and a cad, a boorish lout for upsetting the permanence of married suburbia. No support or admiration was afforded this man who, under great societal pressure to shut up and sit down, blew apart his staid existence and reinvented his life.

Maybe it's cultural brainwashing that we choose to support traditional marriage despite overwhelming evidence that it doesn't work. Or maybe we're not brave enough to engage in alternative thinking. Or maybe it's that the marriage route is lined with wedding planners, caterers, florists, travel agents, parents, and friends who, when standing together and cheering us on, do an admirable job of hiding the elephant in the middle of the dance floor.

The pressure's greater for men like me: "He has commitment issues." "He's gay." "He's never really been in love." I've heard them all. No, I'm not gay (though I'll admit Colin Farrell's cute). Yes, I've fallen in love hard enough to know that those euphoria-inducing endorphins will make you agree to just about anything. And I'll cop to the commitment issues. It's just that I'm not going to invest time and money in something that's doomed from the start, okay?

As the only holdout in my posse of pals, I do feel like the last guy at the poker table, dealing myself solitaire at what was once a rousing house party. I can't have a beer in a bar past midnight with a man my age without his calling his wife to tell her he'll be home soon. I mostly socialize with single twentysomethings now—surely I look like the oldest Mouseketeer. I don't get many of their *O.C.* jokes, but at least I know enough to wear wide-legged jeans.

My current girlfriend is 25 and, thankfully, not wedding planning yet. But when I start finding *Bridal Guide* under the couch, she's out. It's inevitable, and it'll put me back on the market. And let me tell you, it's no picnic for a never-been-married guy like me. Women would rather date a divorcé than a nuptialphobe. He may have bungled it once or twice, but he's still demonstrated the willingness to commit. Me? Why waste the time?

My point: We need a fundamental rethinking of the concept of marriage. I propose a new approach, one more akin to the legal contracts in the TV world.

Let's say you've successfully dated a girl for a while. Rather than agreeing to "till death do you part," you agree to a "time-limited marriage": At regular intervals, you either renew or walk away...and remain friends. You still have the fancy ceremony, the heartfelt toasts from college roommates, and the slew of candlesticks and Calphalon. But you don't have the pressure of permanence or the soul-draining despair of divorce.

Sometimes, it's being told we're not allowed to stray that actually makes us stray. If, on the other hand, there's always the chance to walk away, I bet more couples would opt to stay together. It's human nature. Free will is sexy. Forced togetherness is not.

Most young lovers would probably sign up for an initial 3-year TLM and graduate to a 5-, 7-, then 10-year contract if the marriage was working. Ultimately, this new matrimonial paradigm keeps both partners on their toes. They have to remain focused, working hard for a renewal, which means treating each other with respect and keeping the fire burning with the creative intensity of a first date. This motivational tool works well in business: If you perform well, we won't fire you. If, however, you're told you can never be fired, well, that's communism.

Along the way, if you meet someone who might make a better partner—or if you're just craving some variety—hang tight until your contract expires. Then you can take a whack without breaking your vows. If you don't decide to renew, no sweat. No legal bills, lingering animosity, or social stigma. You instead thank each other for the privilege of cohosting your patch of planetary existence and move on. Every man and woman who has successfully honored his or her contract receives a handsome certificate, suitable for hanging. This way, when a new prospect comes over for the first time, she'll see your impressive history of fair-minded commitment: "Oh, you had a 5-year TLM with Jenny? That's awesome."

You both decide to renew? Congratulations! Now you can throw another party! Your friends and relatives will fly in all over again (bearing more gifts) to celebrate not just the prospect of a fruitful marriage but an actual one in progress. Your cubicle-mates and college chums will take to the microphone, armed with soul-strengthening words of love and support. Who couldn't use the occasional morale boost? I want my dad to stand up and tearfully talk about how proud I've made him. I want my best friend to recount the crazy adventures of yesteryear. I want an iPhoto slide show of my most embarrassing haircuts set to my favorite songs. These tributes are my favorite parts of weddings, but so far, I've never been a recipient, because I won't play by the rules.

I've loved so many amazing women over the years. There was med student Gail, who went from roommate to girlfriend one tequila-fueled night and lasted a good 3 years. And sexy psychotherapist Jen, with whom I had a 5-year, globe-trotting romp. I'll always remember fondly my 3 years with Viv, the tumultuous, top-heavy portraitist who loved as enthusiastically as she drank.

I thought about marrying each of these women, but as the relationships ticked past casual, a big fight would break us up— a big fight about my "I do" aversion. Because I wouldn't drop to one knee, they all end up lumped into the "ex-girlfriend" category, which doesn't come close to defining their importance in my life. I would have TLM'd any of them, and I'd happily display my certificates of achievement today.

Still, everybody asks, "What about the kids?" To which I explain: Who cares? If their parents' contract ends, they're still better off than being stuck in the middle of a traditional divorce. I'd much rather be the spawn of two civil people who didn't renew than see the two genetic codes that created me locked in battle. On the playground, I'd much rather hear "My mommy and daddy didn't renew" than "My mommy and daddy don't talk to each other."

As I write this, about half of my friends' first marriages are, predictably, coming to an end, leaving behind an aftermath of ugliness. It's time to bring some innovation to the sanctity. Let's leave the 19th century behind. It's great to value tradition and all, but slavish adherence in the face of irrefutable evidence of failure is foolish.

So who's in? We just need a few couples to choose a TLM over the traditional route and soon we'll have a wave of converts. I can hear the ceremony now: "Do you, Jack, take Jill to be your lawfully wedded wife for at least 3 wonderful years with the best intention of more, but with the mutual understanding that these forthcoming 3 might be all?"

Let's rock the nation with a resounding chorus of "I do!"

Heal Her with Love

Love doesn't just make you feel good; it can fight disease, boost immunity, and lower stress. Here's how

BY SARAH MAHONEY

WHO DOESN'T LOVE being in love? A true Valentine listens to you vent about work and lets you have that last slice of pizza. She doesn't expect you to watch *Grey's Anatomy*. And she always thinks you're sexy, even in ratty, baggy sweatpants.

Scientists have long been keen to prove that love gives us health benefits, too, both for men and women—beyond the obvious advantage of always having a date for New Year's Eve. Researchers can't say for sure that romance trumps an affectionate family or warm friendships when it comes to wellness. But they are homing in on how sex, kinship, and caring all seem to make us stronger, with health gains that range from faster healing and better control over chronic illnesses to living longer.

The benefits of love are explicit and measurable: A study last year from the University of Pittsburgh found that women in good marriages have a much lower risk of cardiovascular disease than those in high-stress relationships. The National Longitudinal Mortality Study, which has been tracking more than a million subjects since 1979, shows that married people live longer, have fewer heart attacks and lower cancer rates, and even get pneumonia less frequently than singles. And a new study from the University of Iowa found that ovarian cancer patients with a strong sense of connection to others and satisfying relationships had more vigorous "natural killer" cell activity at the site of the tumor than those who didn't have those social ties. (These desirable white blood cells kill cancerous cells as part of the body's immune system.)

Some experts think it won't be long before doctors prescribe steamy sex, romantic getaways, and caring communication in addition to low-cholesterol diets and plenty of rest. If that sounds like a happy Rx, here are ways to make the emerging evidence translate into real-life advice.

THE BENEFITS OF FREQUENT BEAR HUGS

Doctors at the University of North Carolina have found that hugging may dramatically lower blood pressure and boost blood levels of oxytocin, a relaxing hormone. Researchers asked couples to sit close to one another and talk for 10 minutes, then share a long hug; afterward they found positive, albeit small, changes in both blood pressure and oxytocin. But the power of frequent daily hugging was intense: The women with the highest oxytocin levels had systolic blood pressure that was 10 mm Hg lower than women with low oxytocin levels—an improvement similar to the effect of many leading blood pressure medications, says Kathleen Light, PhD, a professor of psychiatry at UNC and one of the study's authors. "Getting more daily hugs from their husbands was related to higher oxytocin, and so the hugs were indirectly related to lower blood pressure," she says. Men didn't get the blood pressure benefit from hugging. (But you probably get the same health gains from steady sex that you do from daily snuggling. A 2002 study from the University of Bristol in England found that men who had sex two or more times a week cut their risk of having a fatal heart attack in half. And a recent study from the National Cancer Institute found that men who ejaculate frequently may be protecting themselves against prostate cancer.)

The hormone oxytocin has been linked to trust, and it helps women bond with everyone from newborns to stockbrokers. But its biggest benefit may turn out to be physical. Breastfeeding has been definitively linked to both lower breast cancer rates and the slower growth of some breast cancer cells; researchers speculate that oxytocin may be responsible. "It is safe to say that oxytocin is linked to emotional as well as physical closeness in partners," Dr. Light says. "And while the healing power of this connection is not yet proven, we think it will be soon."

Oxytocin also surges through the bodies of men and women during orgasm. But whether sex itself directly improves women's health is still not certain. One of the most concrete connections comes from a study by Carl J. Charnetski, PhD, a professor of psychology at Wilkes University and coauthor of *Feeling Good Is Good for You*. In 2004, he measured the immune function of 112 college students, many of whom were in close, loving relationships. Those who had sex with their partner once or twice a week had significantly higher amounts of immunoglobulin A, an antibody that is the body's first line of defense in fighting off disease and infections, than those who had sex less than once a week or not at all. Although making sure you have weekly sex is great health advice, more isn't necessarily better. Dr. Charnetski was surprised to discover that the immune systems of those who had sex three or more times a week were no better off than the no-sex-at-all group. Maybe, he theorizes, "couples who have sex just once a week are simply in healthier, more secure relationships, and have nothing to prove."

Though researchers have yet to link orgasms from masturbation to any measurable physiological gains for women, it's clear that women perceive instant health benefits. Carol Rinkleib Ellison, PhD, a marriage counselor and sex researcher in Oakland, California, and author of *Women's Sexualities*, surveyed 2,632 women from their teens to their 90s and found that two-thirds had masturbated in the previous month. Although most cited the obvious ("because it feels good"), many also gave specific health-related reasons for double-clicking their own mouse—39 percent said it relaxed them, 32 percent said it helped them sleep, and 9 percent said it eased menstrual cramps.

Steady sex may also make women healthier by making relationships happier: When couples are content with their sexual status quo, they've eliminated a big—and extremely stressful—area of conflict. While sex is hardly the only (or even the best) measure of how happy a couple is, it is a kind of romantic superglue. Researchers from the University of Sheffield in England interviewed 28 participants who had been married at least 20 years and found that a consistent sex life continued to be important throughout marriage. "The majority of our participants felt that sex granted their marriage a way to express love, commitment, and trust," says Sharron Hinchliff, PhD, a psychologist, researcher, and author of the study. And when circumstances—a health problem or scheduling change, for instance—made it more difficult for these couples to have sex, they found a way to adapt their sex lives quickly so that they barely noticed the upheaval.

WHY HUMANS WANT AND NEED TO FEEL CLOSE

Experts are quick to point out that sex is only one aspect of connection, and not as powerful as the real magic in relationships: bonding. That sense of being united, even during bad times, is a trait that Brian Baker, a psychiatrist at the University of Toronto, calls cohesion. And his research has found that it's more important to both health and happiness than a good sex life. In one study, he tracked 229 adults who were under job strain. Though they had higher blood pressure at the start, spouses in pleasurable marriages actually lowered systolic blood pressure by 2.5 mm Hg over a 12-month period.

What's more, Baker says, happy couples seem to know almost instinctively that doing things together and spending more time with each other adds to their happiness. It's not that sex didn't matter to these couples. "It's one component of satisfaction," he says. "But couples who had less sex didn't seem to have any less sense of cohesion, and it was their emotional collaboration—their partnership—that kept the marriage strong."

Maybe, Dr. Ellison says, that bond is the brass ring of marriage, enabling us to build a safe cocoon in a world full of difficult bosses, too much traffic, and not enough time. "An ideal relationship gives you a place to come home and recharge your battery. Sitting down with your partner makes you feel calmer. You're in a secure nest, and you're less stressed," she says. "How could that not be good for you?"

THE LOVE RX

Granted, sharing a bond of closeness with your sweetheart feels magical. But a relationship can seem more like a bed of thorns than roses when she's criticizing you over the morning coffee. Most people outgrow the idea that they can change their spouses. But that doesn't mean relationships can't change; couples can learn to fight sweeter, replacing hostile comments with less judgmental ones. "Conflict itself is normal," says Baker, "and it's healthy. It engages couples in the relationship."

But there is a difference between healthy fighting and fighting that wears down your immunity. Studies from the University of Washington show that happy couples manage to be far more positive than negative when they're duking it out, interjecting playful jokes and affectionate pokes in the ribs. In contrast, the I'm-ready-to-break-some-dishes-now anger that comes with fighting causes physiological changes that John Gottman, PhD, executive director of the Relationship Research Institute in Seattle, calls "flooding"; these leave heart rates too high for the couple to come to any effective solution.

Researchers believe that warm interactions between couples can bring about powerful health results, even when one of the partners is battling disease. At the Fox Chase Cancer Center in Philadelphia, Sharon Manne, PhD, studied couples struggling with the wife's breast cancer diagnosis and treatment. Some couples were coached to be more supportive; others muddled through on their own. The wives in the coached group fared better, as measured by their levels of distress and depression. And while Dr. Manne's own research has focused solely on cancer, she thinks couples can use any stressful period to find a friendlier footing.

What worked best? "When partners learned to minimize negative comments and were responsive, and when they were willing to share their own concerns and worries, rather than pretending nothing was wrong . . . that can make a bad marriage good, or a good marriage even better," says Dr. Manne.

In fact, the physiological findings from love research have inspired even the skeptics to change the way they look at relationships—in the lab and at home. "My husband is an immunologist, and when we started our research, he'd be the first to admit that he thought the psychology part of this was a crock," says Janice Kiecolt-Glaser, director of health psychology at Ohio State University's College of Medicine. "Now, he's seen what stress can do in bad relationships, and also how a good relationship can protect people from outside stresses—like work." And it's made the two treasure the time they have to bond. "One of the things we like to do after dinner is to sit with a glass of wine, looking out over the Scioto River. It's clear to us that close relationships are incredibly helpful to our health and well-being."

THE HIGH PRICE OF A BAD RELATIONSHIP

The health benefits of marriage are undeniable. But there's also a dark side: Evidence is mounting that, at least for women, crummy marriages are health vampires, and relationship stress—even more than work stress—undermines the body's physiological defenses.

Couples who handle their disagreements in a negative way, for example, don't heal as well, finds a new study from Ohio State University's Institute for Behavioral Medicine Research. Forty-two couples agreed to have tiny suction wounds made on the palms of their hands. Afterward, they talked to each other about marital sore spots

like money, in-laws, or whether to see *The Pink Panther* or *Tristan &*
Isolde. The couples in happy marriages mended very quickly, while
those in nasty relationships characterized by zingers, sarcasm, and
put-downs healed 40 percent more slowly.

However, the women's bodies proved to be far more sensitive to
hostile remarks than the men's, says Dr. Kiecolt-Glaser, who headed
up the research. "Biologically, the different reactions women have to
a husband who says 'You idiot' versus 'I guess you and I just see this
differently' are enormous," she says. "Women just have a more intense
physiological reaction to hostility in relationships than men do." This
happens, she says, for two reasons: First, women tend to evaluate
negativity in their own relationships accurately, "while men tend to
be semi-oblivious to it." And second, even when the negativity registers with men, "they tend to forget it quickly, while women will often
relive the angry exchanges over and over, for hours."

Evidence of slow-healing wounds is the latest from the lab of
husband-and-wife researchers Kiecolt-Glaser and Ronald Glaser, MD,
an immunologist and director of OSU's Institute for Behavioral Medicine Research. Earlier research by the Glasers had demonstrated
that couples who growled the most at each other had weaker immune
systems for a 24-hour period after tense discussions, with fewer "natural killer" cells and T cells, both key in fighting off illness, and women
were more affected than men.

The researchers have shown that, in addition to affecting cellular activity, discord elevates stress hormones throughout the body.
For that study, the Glasers chose 90 newlywed couples, carefully
screened for their pristine mental and physical health. The lovebirds
were asked to have a tense conversation about a high-conflict subject,
and researchers continually measured their blood for 24 hours for
cortisol and three other leading stress hormones (selected because
they are known to have a direct impact on immunity). Although both
men and women were affected, women's hormones remained high,

sometimes for hours. Not only did the stress hormones stay cranked, but they also predicted divorce: Ten years later, 19 percent of the couples had parted ways. All in this group had higher levels of three of the four stress hormones monitored.

Women don't seem to get used to nastiness and negativity, even in good marriages. The Glasers have also studied happy older couples who had been married an average of 42 years. Just like in the newlyweds, stress hormones increased during conflict, but only for the women.

What has struck Kiecolt-Glaser most over the years about health and relationships, she says, is the way raw biology trumps any Dr. Phil–inspired emotional breakthroughs. "It would be nice if we could just say to ourselves, 'I should be more thick-skinned and not take his remarks so personally,' but women can't seem to shut it off like that. It's not like there's a hearing aid we can yank out of our ears. Our research shows that if the bad feelings and hostility are still alive in you emotionally, then they're still affecting you physically."

Get Back the Lust

Simple strategies for busting out of a lust rut, no matter where you are in your relationship

BY MARGO TROTT

DESPITE THE ENDLESS HYPE about how crucial hot sex is to a happy relationship, few couples on the planet actually do the deed every night. In fact most couples go through periods when one or both partners would rather watch Animal Planet than make the beast with two backs. One study published in the *Journal of Marriage and Family Therapy* found that 24 percent of couples reported having a sexual drought in the past 3 months.

Whether you're stressed, she's tired, or you each have something else on your mind, it's perfectly normal to have the occasional sex-free week. But if you've been low on lust for a little too long, there are plenty of ways to reignite the flames. We identified four phases in relationships when sex drives typically fizzle and asked top experts for the best strategies to get you both back into a steamy groove.

THE NOVELTY HAS OFFICIALLY WORN OFF

When you first met, your mattress springs squeaked on a regular basis and you always had that dewy glow. That's because infatuation triggers the release of extra dopamine, a brain chemical that fuels your libido, says Laura Berman, PhD, director of the Berman Center for sexual health and menopause management in Chicago and author of *The Passion Prescription: Ten Weeks to Your Best Sex—Ever!* When the novelty wears off, so does the dopamine boost, Dr. Berman says.

SCARE YOUR PANTS OFF. Dopamine also kicks in when you're taken by surprise. "Do things that are new and different together, even a little scary," Dr. Berman says. Even a relatively tame act can be a thrill if it's unexpected, says Sherry Amatenstein, relationship expert for iVillage.com and author of *Love Lessons from Bad Break-ups*. Pick up a box of drugstore hair color (the kind that eventually washes out) and go to town on each other. You'll get that sexy hands-on-the-scalp feeling along with the risky excitement of not knowing quite how it's going to turn out.

RESET BOUNDARIES. Sometimes people get so comfortable together they forget that sexual attraction requires a little mystery and excitement, says Mary Ann Donohue, PhD, administrative direc-tor of psychiatric services at Hackensack University Medical Center in New Jersey. Maybe it's time to start closing the bathroom door, burping under your breath, and getting dressed up for a night out the way you used to. And schedule some dates at swank venues—cock-tails at a posh hotel bar or a night at the opera—where you have to dress to impress and act formal. Seeing each other looking your best and surrounded by lights, music, and other couples can bring back the thrill of dating, which will segue into livelier sex when you get home.

YOU'RE ABOUT TO FORSAKE ALL OTHERS

And one, or both, of you is freaking out. Before her wedding, "I was so stressed about losing control over my life," says 33-year-old Stephanie T., who's been married to Joel for 10 years. For some of us, the idea of one sexual partner for a lifetime makes walking bare-foot over thumbtacks sound more appealing than sauntering down the aisle.

JUST DO IT. Sex is how guys say "you're the center of my uni-verse" without having to utter the actual words. "Women may want to shoot me for this, but in an otherwise good relationship, if you some-times go ahead with sex even when you're not in the mood, the ben-efits can be significant," Dr. Berman says. Stop addressing those envelopes and undress each other instead. That 5-minute nooky break tells her she's more important than the florist or the caterer, Dr. Berman says. And it releases oxytocin, a hormone that makes you feel bonded and attached—so you'll remember the reason for those 200 invites in the first place.

LOOK BEYOND THE BIG DAY. Odds are on your side: Married women are more than twice as likely as single ones to have sex two or three times a week, according to a survey by the National Opinion Research Center. And that marriage bond will actually bring you closer. "These last few years we've been very sexually connected," Joel says. What's different? He and Stephanie know each other better. "Now we communicate about intimacy; we make time to do that. We've grown to understand the other person's sexuality and needs better, too."

ONE OF YOU GETS PINK-SLIPPED

"We'd been dating for a year when Matt got fired," says Cynthia B., 41. "He responded by withdrawing; he didn't want to sleep with me." Stress—financial or otherwise—can cause levels of libido-stoking testosterone to drop, says Beverly Whipple, PhD, coauthor of *The G-Spot: And Other Discoveries About Human Sexuality*. And when a guy loses his provider status, it's a blow to his ego and manhood—not exactly the feeling he wants to bring into the bed. If it's the lady who's been canned? Research reported in the *Journal of the American Medical Association* shows that when a woman's income is reduced by just 20 percent, her self-worth and sex drive can plummet.

TACKLE IT TOGETHER. When she's the one taking the hit, form a united front, says Yvonne Thomas, PhD, a psychologist in Los Angeles. Refer to the issue as "ours" instead of "hers," which lets her know you don't blame her. Also make it clear that she hasn't lost any status in your eyes. Remind her how talented and capable she is. Then break out the massage oil and offer to rub her worries away.

THINK DIRTY THOUGHTS. When it's you in the stress-induced slump, talking about sex in a positive way can be powerful, Dr. Berman says. She suggests saying something like "I miss being intimate with you." It can help you recall your last intimate encounter—and all the delicious details—reminding you how good getting naked can make you feel.

YOU'RE BABY BOMBED

Every parent you know points out the irony of having kids: The very act of creating them is unceremoniously sidelined once they're born. "Our toddler has bad dreams a lot and wants to sleep in our bed," Rebecca B., 40, says. Not a sexy threesome.

Sometimes just trying to get the sperm to sidle up to the egg can be enough to make your inner horndog hibernate. Janine L., 34, and Roger L., 35, tried for about a year to have a baby and wound up seeing an infertility specialist. "When you're dealing with a fertility schedule, sex stops being fun," Roger says. "Pair that with having to perform as often as possible during a brief monthly window and you start to lose your steam."

"He felt so much pressure that a couple of times he couldn't 'finish,'" Janine adds. "He'd feel guilty and embarrassed, which only made it worse."

DO IT WHEN IT DOESN'T COUNT. When sex's end result is pure pleasure instead of pregnancy, you have fewer expectations and less likelihood of disappointment. So sneak in non–baby-making sex when you're not ovulating, Dr. Berman says. And if your bedroom has become "fertility central," take the fun-only sex on tour. Your best bet? The closet—where, according to a University of California at Berkeley study, clothes emit a potent chemical from men's sweat, hair, and skin that arouses women. Who knew?

SCHEDULE A GROWN-UPS-ONLY PLAYDATE. Once kids arrive, "getting regular alone time gives you a chance to talk like adults about intimate things," Dr. Whipple says. This may seem obvious, but as Rebecca admits, "We're so busy, it wouldn't happen if we didn't plan it." Sneak away for a day or two every few months. If you've got weather (and geography) on your side, head to the ocean. You'll have uninterrupted time for conversation in the car and—dopamine booster!—you can jump in for a late-night skinny-dip. Even the local Starbucks makes for an easy getaway. Talk like adults over cappuccino and use the caffeine perk for that crucial extra hour after the kids go to bed.

Rut-Proof Your Relationship

Put your humdrum ho-hum into fast-forward

BY VICKI GLEMBOCKI

DO YOU AND YOUR WIFE spend alone time talking about the frequency of your baby's spitting up? Can you and your girlfriend find—at any hour, any night of the week—an episode of *Law & Order* to watch? Are you having "8-Minute Missionary Every Other Tuesday After David Letterman's Opening Monologue" sex? Could be you've slipped (and fallen) into a relationship rut. And you know the old saying: The only difference between a rut and a grave is the depth of the hole.

We're not stuck, you say. We're just comfortable with each other. Maybe so. "One couple's rut may be your fun evening," says Pepper Schwartz, sociology professor at the University of Washington and author of *Between Equals: How Peer Marriage Really Works*. "The question is, How does it feel?" If you're bored, if you'd rather do house-work than do each other, you've probably got some digging to do.

I don't have time, you say. I'm not creative enough. No worries, we brought the shovel. Here's how to rescue yourself from the five routines that plague us most.

ARE WE TURNING ON OUR COMPUTERS AGAIN?

There are people who spend 14 hours at the office; those who work opposite shifts and are mere ships passing in the shower; those who work all day and all night (and all weekend) cleaning, mowing, babying, and making lists of what needs to get done next week.

"The worst part of this rut is that you can actually be considered a champion for being in it, for being so dedicated," says couples coach

Jim Sniechowski, who with his wife, Judith Sherven, cowrote *Be Loved For Who You Really Are: How the Differences Between Men and Women Can Be Turned into the Source of the Very Best Romance You'll Ever Know.* "But you're letting your work be more important than your relationship."

Since most of us can't quit our jobs, we need to make mini-dates with our partner, Sniechowski says. Start small: Meet for lunch once a week, talk for 20 solid minutes at the end of the day, eat breakfast together. Once you've got a routine, get creative.

Jon Cofsky and Abbey Mahady, dating workaholics in Haddonfield, New Jersey, have a "Priceline Party." Every few weeks they wait until 4 p.m. on a weekday and shop Priceline.com for a last-minute hotel deal in nearby Philadelphia. They get to be together, they get to stay in swanky hotels for low rates, and there's only one stipulation: no laptops.

ARE WE GOING TO DINNER AND A MOVIE AGAIN?

Designate a date night, whether it's once a week, every 2 weeks, or every month, and just stick to it, says Mort Fertel, marriage coach and author of *Marriage Fitness.* Always get out of the house. Never invite anyone else. And most important? Never go to any form of entertainment where you have to face in the same direction and aren't supposed to talk. Shoot pool. Go bowling.

"People are always looking for some dramatic, Herculean event that's going to transform the relationship," Fertel says. "That's not necessary." While it might be impressive to schedule a dual spa treatment or head up in a hot air balloon, you'll never beat the intimacy of Fertel's favorite date: going to a coffee shop.

ARE WE FIGHTING ABOUT THE DISHES AGAIN?

"There's nothing more harmful to a relationship than feeling like you're not gaining ground on something," Schwartz says. But we keep getting into the same sweaty ring, swearing that this time we'll throw the knockdown right hook while the crowd cheers, "You go!" Most people argue by launching the same ammo, but expecting different results. That is the real problem. "You need to step back and consider, 'What does she always say before I say that? What does she do before I do that?'" advises Michelle Weiner-Davis, author of *Getting Through to the Man You Love: The No-Nonsense, No-Nagging Guide for Women*. Then, you need to change what you're saying or doing.

Chris and Ally Loprete in Los Angeles were stuck. Whenever she came home from work, he was watching sports. He would ask her how her day was, expecting a one-word answer. She'd launch into a 20-minute vent and, though he would try to listen, he'd glance at the TV, which turned the conversation into a huge, screaming, weekly fight. But when Ally stepped back, she realized she wasn't changing her ammo. So the next time he asked her about her day, she said, "Chris, you are a sweet man. But if you ask me about my day, I'm going to tell you about it. If you want to watch the game, just say, 'Ally, I'll talk to you at the commercial or when the game's over.' Stop trying to be the nice guy, because it's really pissing me off." Bull's-eye.

ARE WE WATCHING *LAW & ORDER* AGAIN?

"When you don't take your hand off the clicker, you're paying more attention to the TV than to your spouse," Fertel says. "Not good." He threw his TV out. And you could too. But what about the game, you say. And the race. Okay. But if you don't want your spouse to become a desperate housewife, agree to watch only 5 hours of TV a week. Or try a weeklong ban. How will you fill the time? Play cards. Put a puzzle together. Talk to each other.

"The TV isn't the problem here," Sniechowski says. A lot of people don't know how to communicate, so they watch TV instead. Sniechowski suggests using the TV as a jumping-off point. Watch

CSI: Miami, Fear Factor, Alias—whatever—and when it's over shut off the TV and talk about the show for a few minutes, even if it's just to balk at couples who are willing to swim through raw sewage. "You'll go on tangents," Sniechowski says. "Eventually, you'll start to look forward to the conversation after the show rather than to the show itself. You might even stop watching the show all together. You won't need it anymore."

IS IT TUESDAY AFTER DAVID LETTERMAN'S OPENING MONOLOGUE AGAIN?

"When sex is good, it's not an issue," says April Masini, relationship advice columnist and author of *Date Out of Your League*. "But when it's bad, it's huge. It's one of the key sources of divorce." First, Masini says, you need to sex up your bedroom. Get rid of the TV. Clear the nightstand of the stacks of magazines and the kids' rectal thermometers. Add aromatherapy candles (try aphrodisiac-prone jasmine or sandalwood), books of erotica (try *The Delta of Venus* by Anais Nin), and a CD player with sexy CDs (try Sarah McLachlan's *Fumbling Towards Ecstasy* or Prince's *Purple Rain*).

Now what?

"Our bodies produce sex chemicals naturally. That's nature helping us hook up," says Ian Kerner, PhD, a certified sex therapist and author of *She Comes First: The Thinking Man's Guide to Pleasuring a Woman*. "When the sex is no longer new, we need to trick the brain into stimulating those chemicals. We need novelty." But it's better to break the ice before breaking the iceberg. Tell each other about sexy dreams you've had. Have sex in a room in which you've never had sex before.

Or go to the gym. Just being in each other's presence during an everyday routine can add fuel to the flame. "Exercising together can be a great way to get the adrenaline flowing," says Logan Levkoff, PhD, a New York City–based sex educator. "You get sweaty, a little competitive, and before you know it, you're in the mood for the between-the-sheets aerobics."

Once you're feeling, well, a little looser, Dr. Kerner suggests you give yourselves a sex-toy assignment. (You each bring home a toy of your choice.) Or role-play. (Remember that fantasy you had about the woman in the produce section? Act that out.)

When Jackie and Dave (not their real names) in Austin, Texas, were longing to re-create the rush of their first kiss, they initiated "Story Nights." They take turns creating personae and scenarios that lead to sex, prepping for the big night with anticipation-building e-mails hinting at how to prepare for the evening (which often involves costumes). "Every night has brought about that raw, horny-teenager sexual tension," Jackie says. "We capture that first-time feeling every time."

QUICKIES

Hash It Out

ARGUMENTS ABOUT MONEY can destroy marriages. Avoid this dismal fate by discussing the subject early and often. Here's a checklist for year 1.

FREE THE SKELETONS. Before you can create budgets or set goals, you have to know where you stand, and that means revealing your complete financial picture to each other. Order credit reports from the three major credit-reporting agencies (TransUnion, Equifax, and Experian). Scores higher than 700 look good to potential lenders. Make a balance sheet of all combined assets and debts. Then devise a payment plan and set rules for using credit cards, says Stewart Welch III, a financial planner and the author of *10 Minute Guide to Personal Finance for Newlyweds*.

LEAVE YOUR W-4'S ALONE. If you each earn more than $78,300, your combined income will make you liable for more taxes. It's called the marriage penalty. Also keep in mind that if you mark "married" on W-4 forms, less of your pay will be withheld. Sounds good now, but consider owing an extra $5,000 next April 15. Hold off on changing your tax forms until you have a good estimate of what you'll owe. "As a rule of thumb, unless you own a home, claim single with one allowance," says Andrew Schwartz, a CPA and the creator of NewlywedFinances.com.

DON'T SHARE EVERYTHING. Merging checkbooks seems simple and smart; it's easier to keep the books if everything flows in and out of one account. The drawback is having to justify that $50 bar tab.

Am I Normal?

I forgave my wife for cheating, but I feel like I can't move on until I confront the guy she was with. Is this a common feeling?

Yes. Your brain works like *SportsCenter*: A highlight is replayed over and over until there's new footage available. If you know him already, confrontation may help you move on. If you've never met him, you could create memory triggers that would make it hard to forget.

"Couples who have been married for a while seem to migrate to one account," Schwartz says. "But do it when you're ready."

SCHEDULE SUMMIT MEETINGS. Meet monthly to review the balance sheet and discuss upcoming expenses. "It helps you stay focused," Welch says. "Most people don't do this, but then again, most people are not financially successful."

Tread Lightly

WANT TO UNDERSTAND the female mind? Rent *Sisterhood of the Travel-ing Pants.*

Want to do it without feeling your testicles recede into your body? Listen to what she's asking you—not what she says, but what she means. "A woman wants the man in her life to see things from her point of view," says Brenda Shoshanna, PhD, author of *The Anger Diet: 30 Days to Stress-Free Living.* "She wants to feel like you're on the same page." Here's a quick guide to dodging any conversational bear trap.

SHE ASKS: "Can you believe Dan cheated on Sarah?"

YOU ANSWER: "What could he have been thinking?"

Doesn't matter if she's talking about friends or TV characters—this is her thinly veiled way of checking your moral compass. In her perfect world, you'd tell her you don't condone cheating under any circumstances, and punctuate your statement with "May his man-hood turn black and fall off." If you're not comfortable with that, simply express concern for the cheatee. "She wants to know you empathize with the woman," says Bonnie Eaker Weil, PhD, author of *Make Up, Don't Break Up.*

SHE ASKS: "Is she pretty?"

YOU ANSWER: "Are you fishing for compliments?"

She could be talking about your ex, your co-worker, or that hot waitress. Whoever the woman, your girlfriend doesn't want to feel threatened. Confront this one head-on, says Lillian Glass, PhD, author of *I Know What You're Thinking: Using the Four Codes of Reading People to Improve Your Life*—but do so with a bit of humor. Then offer her a reassuring ego boost by telling her she's beautiful.

Am I Normal?

I accidentally called my wife my boss's name. He's a guy. Is that normal?

No. It sounds as though you have some issues with your wife and her place of authority in your life. When we mix people up with parents or bosses, we're often revealing something about a relationship—maybe it's concern about pleasing her or irritation that she's bossing you around. Figure out what issues are dancing around in your subconscious and clean them out. Try jotting down the context every time you slip up; then look for a pattern in your entries.

SHE ASKS: "Why is my best friend being such a bitch?"

YOU ANSWER: "I don't blame you for being ticked off."

This one's a catch-22, says Dr. Weil. No woman wants to hear that someone she cares about is a screaming shrew. But she also wants you to be on her side. "You have to validate her feelings, but not necessarily agree with her," advises Dr. Weil. Whatever you do, don't insult the friend (or family member) in the process.

SHE ASKS: "Would you go out with Angelina Jolie?"

YOU ANSWER: "Angelina has fat lips. I prefer yours."

Of course you'd go out with Angelina Jolie. You'd be on her like green on grass. You know it, and your girlfriend knows it. (Just as she'd be nannying the hell out of Jude Law if she had the chance.) "She's trying to pick a fight," says Dr. Weil. Instead of answering either way, find a flaw in the famous hottie. You didn't lie, and you made the woman in your life feel attractive.

Get Away

SINCE YOUR VISION of winter break has morphed from chugging Sex on the Beach in Daytona to just lots of sex on Pratesi bed linen, you've also probably learned the pleasures of getting lost on a desolate sand strip with one incredible woman rather than ogling a multitude. Adulthood has its privileges. In compiling this list of exclusive escapes, we scoured the Americas in search of hideaways that are a cut above their competitors, based upon four criteria: seclusion, sand, setting, and service. So if you're bored with seeing Casper the Friendly Ghost staring back at you from the shaving mirror, pack a carry-on, because you won't even need a full week away from work.

CAP JULUCA, ANGUILLA, LEEWARD ISLANDS: This 179-acre property, with its $1^1/_2$-mile-long, crescent-shaped beach and Moroccan-inspired, whitewashed villas, is the perfect place for cracking open a Robert Ludlum. Beach boys posted like sentries along the sand seem to anticipate your next whim ("Hmmm, Caesar salad and a margarita") and make sure that you're well fed and well hydrated. 264-497-6666, www.capjuluca.com

CARLISLE BAY, ST. MARY'S, ANTIGUA: The sister hotel to London's One Aldwych brings modern touches—an Asian restaurant and a screening room with 45 blue Italian-leather seats—to this otherwise old-school island. No motorized water sports are allowed on the beach for serenity's sake, and sunbathing guests are given cold lemongrass-scented hand towels and iced watermelon slices to stay cool. 268-484-0000, www.carlisle-bay.com

COTTON HOUSE MUSTIQUE, ST. VINCENT AND THE GRENADINES: Tommy Hilfiger and Mick Jagger have made the scene at the Cotton House's Tuesday Night Party. The 20-room resort is the only place to stay on this 1,400-acre island, where A-listers clandestinely decompress in a handful of luxury villas. The hotel's beach is an ivory, crescent-shaped one, and with a new spa, every guest can now be pampered like a rock star. 784-456-4777, www.cottonhouse.net

FOUR SEASONS RESORT, PLACENTIA PAPAGAYO, COSTA RICA: If the sun feels too warm at the beach on protected Culebra Bay, no worries. Just walk 5 minutes to the windswept beach on Virador Bay. The resort is carved into the tip of a rugged peninsula on Costa Rica's northwest coast. Footpaths lead through gardens of native flowers to three swimming pools, the main building, a spa, and a golf course. 011-50-66-96-0000, www.fourseasons.com/costarica

IKAL DEL MAR, YUCATAN PENINSULA, MEXICO: The Riviera Maya, an 80-mile stretch of sand set between the jungle of the Yucatan Peninsula and the Caribbean, has spots like Cancun with wall-to-wall chain hotels. Thirty minutes south, though, unspoiled gems like Ikal del Mar still exist—29 thatch-roofed villas, a beach dotted with palapa-roofed cabanas, a short pier for swimming, and a terrace that houses the restaurant. 52-984-877-3000, www.ikaldelmar.com

PARROT CAY, PARROT CAY, TURKS AND CAICOS: You know you're not heading to just any Caribbean resort when a speedboat whisks you from Providenciales in Turks and Caicos to reach the 1,000-acre private enclave known as Parrot Cay. The suspicion is affirmed when you check in to one of the 60 rooms, many with their own stretch of white

What Men Want from Their Marriages

54 percent of men want to spend more quality time with the missus.

79 percent want some of that quality time to be in the sack.

32 percent want to have fewer arguments.

14 percent would settle for fewer "big discussions".

sand facing the open blue sea. In the evening, you can eat a candlelit dinner beside the pool. 649-946-7788, www.parrotcay.como.bz

PINK SANDS BEACH, HARBOUR ISLAND, BAHAMAS: Crushed coral is what gives this 3-mile stretch of shoreline its name. Here palm trees outnumber people, the reef-protected waters are almost always calm, and the temperature hovers between the mid-70s and low 80s. When you tire of hanging at the resort's 25 pastel cottages, head into Dunmoretown and dine with the locals on the lawn at Angela's Starfish Restaurant. 800-688-7678, www.islandoutpost.com

SALTWHISTLE BAY CLUB, MAYREAU, THE GRENADINES: The Saltwhistle Bay Club is the only hotel on Mayreau, a 3-square-mile spit of land in the Grenadines. Its 10 guest suites lie within a 23-acre tropical garden at the island's northern tip. The property's western side spills into the Atlantic, where steady breezes create a windsurfing hot spot, but the heart of the club is the thatch-roofed beach bar on the Caribbean side. 784-458-8444, www.saltwhistlebay.com

TURTLE INN, PLACENTIA PENINSULA, BELIZE: If the impeccable Turtle Inn—with 18 thatch-roofed Balinese cabanas, a Thai spa, and Indonesian gardens on an alabaster Caribbean beach—seems like a movie set, there's good reason. It's owned by filmmaker Francis Ford Coppola. Each cabana has a private tropical garden with an outdoor shower, perfect for making your own movies—be they PG or NC-17. 800-746-3743, www.turtleinn.com

Enjoy These Marriage Perks

A BENEFIT TO BUYING THE COW: Married men do less housework than men who live with their girlfriends, according to a study published in the *Journal of Family Issues*. Part of the reason may be that live-in couples have more of an "incomplete" relationship, compared with the structure of marriage, and that provides more freedom for partners to negotiate roles.

But don't shirk all domestic duties. Taking out the trash could kick high blood pressure to the curb. Researchers reporting in the journal *Medicine & Science in Sports & Exercise* discovered that performing household chores reduces blood pressure. The scientists equipped 28 people with BP monitors and accelerometers to measure calorie expenditure, then asked each person to do 150 calories' worth of housework daily. After 2 days, their BP levels fell an average of 13 points. And while the reductions lasted only 8 hours, daily chores could lower BP long-term, says lead author Jaume Padilla, MS.

ASK THE GIRL NEXT DOOR

The honest truth about women from our lovely neighbor

What can I do to get my wife interested in morning sex?

Being poked awake is daunting. How can a girl catch up with that level of horniness when seconds ago she was dreaming about losing her luggage? And even if she's a little randy, women aren't as proficient at blocking out antiaphrodisiacs like morning breath and eye boogers. Still, there is one move that gets me going on even my groggiest mornings. Try this persuasive maneuver on your barely awake beauty: Lie on your side and initiate a full-frontal cuddle. Pepper her cheeks and lips with gentle kisses as you sling her leg over your hip and slide what you've got up against where you want it to be. Leave it there as you continue to kiss her and caress her butt and thigh. There are a lot of psychological aspects to sex, but a warm suggestion between a woman's legs can send a signal that bypasses the brain and goes straight to the clitoris. The second she moves her hips, you'll know you have her hooked.

My wife says she doesn't want anything for Christmas. Is she serious?

Of course not. What she means is that she isn't going to give you any ideas. Think up something great on your own and score major credit. Skip all things practical and go for pure entertainment or high-end pampering: tickets to a play or concert you have to dress up for, a gift certificate for a massage. (Put the certificate in a box and wrap it.) If she prefers the latest thing—purple is in—she'd probably melt for a 24-inch chain (silver or gold, depending on what she wears most) with a teardrop-shaped amethyst pendant.

Leaving the toilet seat up: Really, what's the big deal?
The truth is that most women who make a fuss about whether the
seat Is up or down don't really care about the seat. (Any girl who sits
without looking gets what she deserves.) It's just a symbolic gesture
we use to gauge how considerate you are in general. If you take the
time to lower the seat, you'll probably also take the time to call if
you're going to be late, offer your jacket when it's cold, or run to the
store at 3 a.m. when we're pregnant and hankering for butter pecan.

**What would a woman think if a man asked her to perform with him
on camera?**
In the context of a great, trusting relationship, it would be a fun,
naughty way to spend a Saturday night. But I'd have to be feeling
extremely good about my body. My friends agree that if they were to
watch a video of themselves having sex, they'd be too busy critiquing
their jiggling thighs or soft tummies to actually draw any pleasure
from it. Personally, I'd insist on low lighting, a flattering black-and-
white effect, and first rights to view it so I could decide whether my
boyfriend got to see it or not. And then, at the end of the night, I'd be
sure to erase it. As my sister said, "Those tapes always end up in the
wrong hands."

Is Your Wife Happy?

HERE'S A SIMPLE test to find out.

> **1. How does your wife act when she's mad at you?**
> a. She comes out fighting.
> b. She gives me the silent treatment.
> c. She never gets mad at me.

"Women fight until they've given up hope," says Diane Sollee, director of Smartmarriages.com. In other words, if she's completely agreeable, you're screwed.

> **2. The deepest conversation you've had with her in the past month involved . . .**
> a. Growing up in Lake Wobegon (you or her)
> b. Retiring to St. Lucia someday (you and her)
> c. How much you hate the bedspread

"Not talking about the past or future anymore is a sign of danger," says Terry Real, author of *How Can I Get Through to You? Closing the Intimacy Gap Between Men and Women*. "Talking renews a relationship."

> **3. When you go to bed, she . . .**
> a. Hits the sack, too
> b. Flips on Leno
> c. Goes out

"If you're out of sync," says Lou Paget, author of *365 Days of Sensational Sex*, "it's a symptom of larger issues. She's distancing herself from you."

4. Last time you were promoted, what did you two do that night?

a. Each other

b. Went out for a fancy dinner

c. Caught a *Newlyweds* marathon

"Your success is her success," says Paget. "She shouldn't see your commitment to your job as selfish." Make sure she understands you work so hard because you're putting the marriage on a firm financial footing.

5. How well do you know your wife's best friend?

a. Not biblically. We hang out.

b. She's going when I'm coming.

c. I hope to meet her someday.

If you're getting the cold shoulder from her friends, your wife is likely dishing about you. It's a sign she's giving up on the marriage, says Michele Weiner-Davis, founder of Divorcebusting.com.

SCORING

a = 3 points, b = 2 points, c = 1 point

12–15 POINTS: Like a trucker on speed, you're in it for the long haul.

9–11 POINTS: Your marriage is on solid ground, but watch for signs of trouble, like the TiVo-ing of *Desperate Housewives*.

5–8 POINTS: Hope you still have your hair.

INDEX

Underscored page references indicate boxed text.